LEAVING CERTI

LESS STRESS MORE SUCCESS

Maths Revision
Ordinary Level
Paper 1

Brendan Guildea & Louise Boylan

g GILL EDUCATION

Gill Education

Hume Avenue

Park West

Dublin 12

www.gilleducation.ie

Gill Education is an imprint of M.H. Gill & Co.

© Brendan Guildea and Louise Boylan 2013

978 07171 4694 9

The paper used in this book is made from the wood pulp of managed forests.
For every tree felled, at least one tree is planted, thereby renewing natural resources.

Any links to external websites should not be construed as an endorsement by Gill
Education of the content or view of the linked material.

For permission to reproduce photographs, the authors and publisher gratefully
acknowledge the following:

© Shutterstock: 21, 30, 39, 43, 46, 60, 63, 80, 95, 140, 156, 169, 228;
© Shutterstock/Adriano Castelli: 74; © Shutterstock/titus manea: 161.

The authors and publisher have made every effort to trace all copyright holders, but if
any has been inadvertently overlooked we would be pleased to make the necessary
arrangement at the first opportunity.

CONTENTS

Please note:
- The philosophy of Project Maths is that topics can overlap, so you may encounter Paper 1 material on Paper 2 and vice versa.
- The Exam questions marked by the symbol  in this book are selected from the following:
  1. SEC Exam papers
  2. Sample exam papers
  3. Original and sourced exam-type questions

Introduction

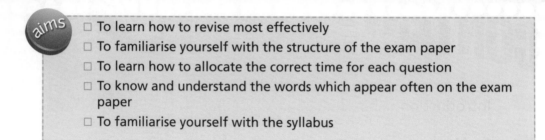

The aim of this revision book is to help you get as high a mark as possible in your Leaving Certificate. This book is designed to be exam focused. To do this, the book is based not just on the syllabus, but also on the examination paper. As a result, this revision book can be used in conjunction with **any** textbook.

Throughout this book, **examples and exam-type questions are graded by level of difficulty**.

This level of difficulty is indicated by calculator symbols, as follows:

The number of calculators shown beside a question helps you know how difficult the question is. One calculator indicates a question which is relatively basic. As the questions get harder the symbol will have more calculators. Three calculators indicates an average, level question, whereas five calculators indicates that it is a very challenging question. These questions may be beyond some students, but give them a go! **Students hoping to achieve an A grade should aim to complete all of the five calculator questions**. The calculator symbol given for each question relates to the most difficult part of that question. **Do not be discouraged by a challenging question**. As in the Leaving Certificate exam, difficult questions can sometimes begin with one or two simple parts. You should attempt as much as you can.

It is very important to realise that **you are your own best teacher**. Revision is when you begin to teach yourself. Thus, it is very important for you to start your revision as soon as possible. Make notes while you are revising. If you are having difficulty with a particular question, seek help from your teacher, a friend or a member of your family. As with all subjects, the best examination preparation is to work through past examination or sample papers so that you are familiar with the layout and style of questions.

Let's start at the beginning. If you want to do well in your Leaving Certificate, then two things are essential:

- Revise effectively.
- Be familiar with the exam paper and so be prepared on the day of the exam.

These may seem obvious, but it's worth taking a moment to think about what these tips mean.

How to revise most effectively

If you are going to do well in the Leaving Certificate, you are going to spend quite a bit of time revising. Spending a little time learning how to revise effectively will help you get more from your time and help you absorb and understand more of the material on the course. Here are some tips to help you revise for maths.

- Find a quiet place where you can work. This place should be dedicated to study, free of potential distractions. Turn off all the music the TV, computer and mobile phone.

- Draw up a study plan. Don't be afraid to ask your parents/teachers/guidance counsellor for help at this stage.

- Do the more challenging revision first, when you are fresh. Trying to focus on difficult problems when you are tired can be counter-productive.

- Project Maths is based on understanding, so while you can learn some elements of the course, it is important that you develop an understanding of the material.

Study in small chunks lasting 25 to 35 minutes. Your memory and concentration will work better if you study in short, frequent, bursts.

- Drill and practice are essential ingredients for success in maths.

- Try to link any new material to things you know already. This is learning through association and helps long-term retention.

key point

Don't get hung up on more difficult material. Concentrate on understanding the fundamental concepts and being able to answer all of the straightforward questions. Then, with time, you can build up to the more challenging problems.

Leaving Certificate examination

Exam focus is critical to exam success. It is important to prepare yourself for the challenge you will face. By learning about the structure of the exam, you will learn how to maximise your points, allocate your time effectively and to manage the paper without panic.

The order of the questions is not set and some questions may include cross-syllabus topics. The examination paper will be presented in two sections, as follows:

Section A – 150 marks
Concepts and Skills

Section B – 150 marks
Contexts and Applications

Read the exam paper right through at the start in order to determine which question is the easiest one to begin with. Your mind may also be subconsciously processing some of the problems.

Start with your best question, then your next best and so on. This way, if you are short of time, at least your best questions will be done.

Time yourself as follows

- Reading the paper at the start: 5 minutes

- Section A: 70 minutes

- Section B: 70 minutes

Rule of thumb for timing yourself during the exam:

- Reviewing your answers at the end: 5 minutes

Time spent on question = ½ (marks for question)

- Try to stick closely to these times. If you run out of time on a question, leave it and come back at the end.

That is, a 25-mark question should take no more than 12·5 minutes.

Further exam tips

- There is no such thing as 'rough work' in maths – all work is relevant. If the examiner doesn't know how you reached an answer, even a correct answer, then full marks will not usually be awarded. Thus, **show all your work**.

- Attempt marks (partial credit) will be awarded for any step in the right direction. Therefore, **make an attempt at each part of the question**. Even if you do not get the correct answer, you can still pick up most of the marks on offer if you show how you worked it out. Also, **draw a diagram where possible**, because this can help you see the solution.

Attempt marks (partial credit) are valuable, so it is vital that you attempt all questions. Leave **NO** blanks.

- If you cannot finish part of a question, leave a space and come back to it later. **Never scribble out any work or use Tipp-Ex**. Put a single line through it so that the examiner can still read it. In many cases, work that has a line through it can receive more marks than the candidate's other attempts.

- **Avoid using pencil** because the writing can be very faint and difficult to read.

- It is a good idea to show each stage of a calculation when using a calculator (in case you press a wrong key). Familiarise yourself with your calculator. Know your book of tables and formulae well and write down any formula that you use.

Your calculator and book of tables and formulae are two extremely valuable resources to have in the exam. Make sure that you are very familiar with how your calculator works and that you know how to perform all functions on it. Also familiarise yourself with the book of tables and formulae so that you don't waste any time in the exam trying to find formulae.

Glossary of words used on the examination paper

Write down, state
You can write down your answer without showing any work. However, if you want you can show some workings.

Calculate, find, show that, determine, prove
Obtain your answers by showing all relevant work. Marks are available for showing the steps leading to your final answer or conclusion.

Solve
Find the solution, or root, of an equation. The solution is the value of the variable that makes the left-hand side balance with the right-hand side.

Evaluate
Usually to work out, or find, a numerical value by putting in numbers for letters.

Comment on
After studying the given information or your answers, give your opinion on their significance.

Plot

Indicate the position of points on a graph, usually on the *x*- and *y*-planes.

Construct

Draw an accurate diagram, usually labelled, using a pencil, ruler, set square, compass and protractor. Leave all construction marks on your diagram.

Sketch

Make a rough diagram or graph, labelled if needed.

Hence

You *must* use the answer, or result, from the previous part of the question.

Hence or otherwise

It is recommended that you use the answer, or result, from the previous part of the question, but other methods are acceptable.

Syllabus and checklist for Leaving Certificate Ordinary Level Maths Paper 1 exam

The philosophy of Project Maths is that topics can overlap, so you may encounter Paper 2 material on Paper 1 and vice versa.

Throughout your course you will be asked to apply your knowledge and skills to solve problems in familiar and unfamiliar contexts. In problem solving, you should use some of the following strategies:

- trial and improvement
- draw a diagram
- look for a pattern
- act it out
- draw a table
- simplify the problem
- use an equation
- work backwards
- eliminate possibilities.

The syllabus stresses that in all aspects of the Leaving Certificate Maths course, students should be able to:

☐ Explore patterns and formulate conjectures.

☐ Explain findings.

☐ Justify conclusions.

☐ Communicate mathematics verbally and in written form.

☐ Apply their knowledge and skills to solve problems in familiar and unfamiliar contexts.

☐ Analyse information presented verbally and translate it into mathematical form.

☐ Devise, select and use appropriate mathematical models, formulae or techniques to process information and to draw relevant conclusions.

Number systems

☐ Recognise irrational numbers and appreciate that $\mathbb{R} \neq \mathbb{Q}$.

☐ Revisit the operations of addition, multiplication, subtraction and division in the following domains:

  ○ $\mathbb{N}$ of natural numbers

  ○ $\mathbb{Z}$ of integers

  ○ $\mathbb{Q}$ of rational numbers

  ○ $\mathbb{R}$ of real numbers

  and represent these numbers on a number line.

☐ Develop decimals as special equivalent fractions strengthening the connection between these numbers and fraction and place value understanding.

☐ Consolidate your understanding of factors, multiples, prime numbers in $\mathbb{N}$.

☐ Express numbers in terms of their prime factors.

☐ Appreciate the order of operations, including brackets.

☐ Work with irrational numbers.

☐ Express non-zero positive rational numbers in the form $a \times 10^n$, where $n \in \mathbb{Z}$ and $1 \leq a < 10$ and perform arithmetic operations on numbers in this form.

Expressions

☐ Evaluate expressions given the value of the variables.

☐ Expand and simplify expressions.

☐ Factorise expressions of order 2.

☐ Add and subtract expressions of the form:

  ○ $(ax + by + c) \pm ... \pm (dx + ey + f)$

  ○ $(ax^2 + bx + c) \pm ... \pm (dx^2 + ex + f)$ where $a, b, c, d, e, f \in \mathbb{Z}$.

  ○ $\dfrac{a}{bx + c} \pm \dfrac{q}{px + r}$ where $a, b, c, p, q, r \in \mathbb{Z}$

☐ Use the associative and distributive properties to simplify expressions of the form:

  ○ $(bx + cy + d) \pm ... \pm e(fx + gy + h)$

  ○ $(x \pm y)(w \pm z)$

☐ Rearrange formulae.

Solving equations

☐ Select and use suitable strategies (graphic, numeric, algebraic, mental) for finding solutions to equations of the form:

   ○ $f(x) = g(x)$ with $f(x) = ax + b$ and $g(x) = cx + d$, where $a, b, c, d \in \mathbb{Q}$

   ○ $f(x) = g(x)$

      with $f(x) = \dfrac{a}{bx + c} \pm \dfrac{q}{px + r}$; $g(x) = \dfrac{c}{f}$ where $a, b, c, d, e, f, p, q, r \in \mathbb{Z}$

   ○ $f(x) = k$ with $f(x) = ax^2 + bx + c$ (and not necessarily factorisable)

   ○ where $a, b, c \in \mathbb{Q}$

     and interpret the results.

☐ Select and use suitable strategies (graphic, numeric, algebraic, mental) for finding solutions to:

   ○ simultaneous linear equations with two unknowns and interpret the results.

   ○ one linear equation and one equation of order 2 with two unknowns (restricted to the case where either the coefficient of x or the coefficient of y equals 1 in the linear equation) and interpret the results.

☐ Form quadratic equations given whole number roots.

Inequalities

☐ Select and use suitable strategies (graphic, numeric, algebraic, mental) for finding solutions to inequalities of the form:

   ○ $g(x) \le k, g(x) \ge k$, where $g(x) = ax + b$ where $a, b, k \in \mathbb{Q}, x \in \mathbb{R}$.

Indices

☐ Solve problems using the rules for indices.

Functions

☐ Recognise that a function assigns a unique output to a given input.

☐ Graph functions of the form:

   ○ ax where $a \in \mathbb{Q}, x \in \mathbb{R}$

   ○ $ax + b$ where $a, b \in \mathbb{Q}, x \in \mathbb{R}$

   ○ $ax^2 + bx + c$ where $a, b, c \in \mathbb{Z}, x \in \mathbb{R}$

   ○ $ax^3 + bx^2 + cx + d$ where $a, b, c, d \in \mathbb{Z}, x \in \mathbb{R}$

   ○ ab^x where $a \in \mathbb{N}, b, x \in \mathbb{R}$.

☐ Interpret equations of the form $f(x) = g(x)$ as a comparison of the above functions.

☐ Use graphical methods to find approximate solutions to:

- $f(x) = 0$
- $f(x) = k$
- $f(x) = g(x)$

where $f(x)$ and $g(x)$ are of the above form, or where graphs of $f(x)$ and $g(x)$ are provided.

☐ Form composite functions.

☐ Investigate the concept of the limit of a function.

Complex numbers

☐ Investigate the operations of addition, multiplication, subtraction and division with complex numbers $\mathbb{C}$ in rectangular form $a + ib$.

☐ Illustrate complex numbers on an Argand diagram.

☐ Interpret the modulus as distance from the origin on an Argand diagram and calculate the complex conjugate.

Patterns, sequences and series

☐ Appreciate that processes can generate sequences of numbers or objects.

☐ Investigate patterns among these sequences.

☐ Use patterns to continue the sequence.

☐ Generate rules or formulae from those patterns.

☐ Generalise and explain patterns and relationships in algebraic form.

☐ Recognise whether a sequence is arithmetic, geometric or neither.

☐ Find the sum to n terms of an arithmetic series.

☐ Verify and justify formulae from number patterns.

Arithmetic (financial maths)

☐ Check a result by considering whether it is of the right order of magnitude and by working the problem backwards. Round off a result.

☐ Make and justify estimates and approximations of calculations; calculate percentage error and tolerance.

☐ Calculate average rates of change (with respect to time).

☐ Make estimates of measures in the physical world around you.

☐ Accumulate error (by addition or subtraction only).

Solve problems that involve:

- costing: materials, labour and wastage
- metric system; change of units; everyday imperial units (conversion factors provided for imperial units)
- cost price

- selling price
- loss
- discount
- mark - up (profit as a % of cost price)
- margin (profit as a % of selling price)
- compound interest
- depreciation (reducing balance method)
- income tax and net pay (including other deductions).

Calculus

- [ ] Find first and second derivatives of linear, quadratic and cubic functions by rule.
- [ ] Associate derivatives with slopes and tangent lines.
- [ ] Apply differentiation to:
  - rates of change
  - maxima and minima
  - curve sketching.

1 Algebra

aims

☐ To learn how to evaluate expressions
☐ To learn how to simplify algebraic expressions
☐ To learn how to factorise expressions
☐ To learn how to change the subject of a formula
☐ To learn how to work with irrational numbers

Evaluating expressions

To evaluate expressions, given the value of the variables, substitute the values in for the variables and evaluate the expression.

Example

Find the value of $5(2a - b)$ when $a = -3$ and $b = 7$.

Solution

$5(2a - b)$
$= 5(2(-3) - (7))$ (let $a = -3$ and $b = 7$)
$= 5(-6 - 7)$
$= 5(-13)$
$= -65$

key point

Take care when substituting in negative values. Always put brackets around these, then simplify the expression.

Example

Find the value of $p^2 - 6pq$ when $p = -2$ and $q = 3$.

Solution

$p^2 - 6pq$
$= (-2)^2 - 6(-2)(3)$ (let $p = -2$ and $q = 3$)
$= 4 - 6(-6)$ $((-2)^2 = (-2)(-2) = +4)$
$= 4 + 36$
$= 40$

exam focus

Evaluating expressions is a vital skill for you to have throughout all aspects of your maths course.

Find the value of $\dfrac{2x - y + 3}{x^2 + 2y}$ when $x = \dfrac{3}{2}$ and $y = \dfrac{2}{3}$.

Solution

$$\dfrac{2x - y + 3}{x^2 + 2y}$$

$$= \dfrac{2\left(\dfrac{3}{2}\right) - \left(\dfrac{2}{3}\right) + 3}{\left(\dfrac{3}{2}\right)^2 + 2\left(\dfrac{2}{3}\right)} \qquad \left(\text{let } x = \dfrac{3}{2} \text{ and } y = \dfrac{2}{3}\right)$$

$$= \dfrac{3 - \dfrac{2}{3} + 3}{\dfrac{9}{4} + \dfrac{4}{3}} \qquad \text{(use calculator)}$$

$$= \dfrac{\dfrac{16}{3}}{\dfrac{43}{12}} \qquad \text{(add the fractions on the top and bottom)}$$

$$= \dfrac{16}{3} \times \dfrac{12}{43} \qquad \text{(turn the bottom fraction upside-down and multiply)}$$

$$= \dfrac{192}{129}$$

$$= \dfrac{64}{43} \qquad \text{(simplify by dividing 3 into the top and bottom)}$$

Simplifying algebraic expressions

You must be able to apply the associative and distributive properties when simplifying algebraic expressions.

Associative property	Distributive property
$(A \times B) \times C = A \times (B \times C)$	$A(B + C) = AB + AC$
	$(A + B)(C + D) = A(C + D) + B(C + D)$

Example

Simplify $5(4x - 1) - 3(2x - 5)$.

Solution

$5(4x - 1) - 3(2x - 5)$ (remember $-3 \times -5 = 15$)

$20x - 5 - 6x + 15$ (multiply out the brackets)

$14x + 10$ (add like terms)

key point

Add and subtract like terms.

Example

Simplify $2a(4a + 3) - 4(3a - 7)$

Solution

$2a(4a + 3) - 4(3a - 7)$

$8a^2 + 6a - 12a + 28$ (multiply out the brackets)

$8a^2 - 6a + 28$ (add like terms)

Example

Simplify $(2x + 3)(x - 4)$.

key point

There are two methods for multiplying out brackets. These are both shown in this example. You can use whichever method you prefer.

Solution

Method 1: use distributive law

$(2x + 3)(x - 4)$

$2x(x - 4) + 3(x - 4)$ (remember $+3 \times -4 = -12$)

$2x^2 - 8x + 3x - 12$ (multiply out the brackets)

$2x^2 - 5x - 12$ (add like terms)

Method 2: use box method

Put the terms in the first bracket on the top and terms from the second bracket down the side. Multiply each term by each other term.

	$2x$	$+3$
x	$2x^2$	$+3x$
-4	$-8x$	-12

Listing all terms from inside the boxes:

$2x^2 - 8x + 3x - 12$

$2x^2 - 5x - 12$ (add like terms)

Example

Simplify $(3p + 2q)(p - 3q)$.

Solution

$(3p + 2q)(p - 3q)$

$3p(p - 3q) + 2q(p - 3q)$ (using distributive law)

$3p^2 - 9pq + 2pq - 6q^2$ (multiply out the brackets)

$3p^2 - 7pq - 6q^2$ (add like terms)

Example

Simplify $(5a - 7)^2$.

Solution

$(5a - 7)^2 = (5a - 7)(5a - 7)$

	$5a$	-7
$5a$	$25a^2$	$-35a$
-7	$-35a$	$+49$

$25a^2 - 35a - 35a + 49$ (using box method)

$25a^2 - 70a + 49$ (add like terms)

Simplify $(3x - 4)(x^2 + 3x - 6)$.

Solution

$(3x - 4)(x^2 + 3x - 6)$

$3x(x^2 + 3x - 6) - 4(x^2 + 3x - 6)$

$3x^3 + 9x^2 - 18x - 4x^2 - 12x + 24$ (multiply out the brackets)

$3x^3 + 5x^2 - 30x + 24$ (add like terms)

Adding algebraic fractions

You must put each fraction over the lowest common multiple (LCM) of the denominators. The LCM is the smallest number or expression that all denominators divide into evenly.

Example

Simplify $\dfrac{x + 3}{2} + \dfrac{2x - 1}{5}$.

Solution

$\dfrac{5(x + 3) + 2(2x - 1)}{10}$ (LCM of the denominators 2 and 5 is 10)

$\dfrac{5x + 15 + 4x - 2}{10}$ (multiply out brackets)

$\dfrac{9x + 13}{10}$ (simplify)

Simplify $\dfrac{x - 4}{3} - \dfrac{3x - 1}{6} + \dfrac{2x + 5}{4}$.

Solution

$\dfrac{4(x - 4) - 2(3x - 1) + 3(2x + 5)}{12}$ (LCM of the denominators 3, 6 and 4 is 12)

$\dfrac{4x - 16 - 6x + 2 + 6x + 15}{12}$ (multiply out brackets)

$\dfrac{4x + 1}{12}$ (simplify)

Example

Simplify $\dfrac{3}{p + 2} + \dfrac{5}{p - 1}$.

Solution

$\dfrac{3(p - 1) + 5(p + 2)}{(p + 2)(p - 1)}$ (LCM of the denominators $(p + 2)$ and $(p - 1)$ is $(p + 2)(p - 1)$)

$\dfrac{3p - 3 + 5p + 10}{(p + 2)(p - 1)}$ (multiply out brackets)

$\dfrac{8p + 7}{(p + 2)(p - 1)}$ (simplify)

Example

Simplify $\dfrac{2}{x-3} - \dfrac{7}{2x+5} + \dfrac{2}{3}$.

Solution

Common denominator of $(x-3)$, $(2x+5)$ and 3 is $(x-3)(2x+5)(3)$:

$$\frac{2(2x+5)(3) - 7(x-3)(3) + 2(x-3)(2x+5)}{(x-3)(2x+5)(3)}$$

$$\frac{2(6x+15) - 7(3x-9) + 2(2x^2+5x-6x-15)}{(x-3)(2x+5)(3)} \qquad \text{(multiply out brackets on top)}$$

$$\frac{12x+30 - 21x+63 + 2(2x^2-1x-15)}{(x-3)(2x+5)(3)} \qquad \text{(multiply out brackets on top)}$$

$$\frac{-9x+93 + 4x^2 - 2x - 30}{(x-3)(2x+5)(3)} \qquad \text{(multiply out brackets on top)}$$

$$\frac{4x^2 - 11x + 63}{(x-3)(2x+5)(3)} \qquad \text{(simplify)}$$

Factorising and simplifying expressions

There are four types of factorising that we will meet on this course:

Take out common terms	Factorising by grouping
$ab + ad = a(b + d)$	$ab + ad + cb + cd = (a + c)(b + d)$
Factorise a trinomial	**Difference of two squares**
$a^2 - 2ab + b^2 = (a - b)(a - b)$	$a^2 - b^2 = (a + b)(a - b)$

exam focus

Factorising is a basic and vital skill for you to have throughout your maths course. You must be able to factorise expressions quickly and easily. This will take practice, but it is worth spending time on.

1. Take out common terms

1. Find the highest common factor (HCF) of all the terms making up the expression. This is the biggest value (constants or variables) that divides into all terms evenly.
2. Put the HCF outside the brackets.
3. Divide each term by the HCF to find the factor inside the brackets.

Example

Factorise the following:

(i) $3p^2 + 6pq$

(ii) $ab - 2a^2b + 3ab^2$

Solution

(i) $3p^2 + 6pq$ (HCF is $3p$)

   $3p(p + 2q)$ (factorise out $3p$)

(ii) $ab - 2a^2b + 3ab^2$

   $ab - 2aab + 3abb$ (HCF is ab)

   $ab(1 - 2a + 3b)$ (factorise out ab)

2. Factorising by grouping

Use this method when you have four terms, with no common factor.

1. Group into pairs with a common factor.
2. Take out the HCF in each pair separately.
3. Take out the new common factor.

Example

Factorise the following:

(i) $3pr - 3ps + qr - qs$

(ii) $a^2 + xy - ay - ax$

Solution

(i) $3pr - 3ps + qr - qs$ (already in pairs with a common factor)

   $3p(r - s) + q(r - s)$ (take out common factor in each pair)

   $(r - s)(3p + q)$ (take out the common factor)

(ii) $a^2 + xy - ay - ax$ (no common factors in the first pair; need to rearrange)

$a^2 - ay + xy - ax$ (rearrange order of the terms so that they are grouped into pairs with a common factor)

$a(a - y) - x(-y + a)$ (take out common factor in each pair)

$a(a - y) - x(a - y)$

$(a - y)(a - x)$ (take out the common factor $(a - y)$)

3. Quadratic trinomials

An expression in the form $ax^2 + bx + c$, where a, b and c are numbers, is called a quadratic trinomial. This is because in the expression, the highest power of x is 2 (quadratic) and it contains three terms (trinomial).

For factorising, quadratic trinomials can be broken into two types:

1. **Final term, c, is positive**

   When the final term is positive, the signs inside the middle of the brackets will be the **same** (either two pluses or two minuses). Keep the sign of the middle term given in the question.

2. **Final term, c, is negative**

   When the final term is negative, the signs inside the middle of the brackets will be **different**.

key point

Use trial and improvement to find the factors. Multiply the inside terms, multiply the outside terms and add the results to see if you get the middle term of the original quadratic trinomial.

Example

Factorise the following:

(i) $x^2 - 7x + 10$ (ii) $2x^2 - 9x - 5$

Solution

(i) $x^2 - 7x + 10$ (final term is positive, so the signs in the brackets are the same)

    $(x - 2)(x - 5)$

Check: outside terms $= (x)(-5) = -5x$
inside terms $= (-2)(x) = \underline{-2x}$
sum $= \qquad\qquad -7x =$ middle term of original quadratic trinomial

Therefore, factors $(x - 2)(x - 5)$ are correct.

Alternative method:

$1x^2 - 7x + 10 \qquad\qquad 1 \times 10 = 10$

M   A   M

$1x^2 - 2x - 5x + 10$

$x(x - 2) - 5(x - 2)$

$(x - 2)(x - 5)$

This is the guide number. It tells you that both signs are the same.

M = 10	A = −7
1 × 10 = 10	1 + 10 = 11
2 × 5 = 10	2 + 5 = 7
−2 × −5 = 10	−2 − 5 = −7

(ii) $2x^2 - 9x - 5$ (final term is negative, so the signs in the brackets are different)

$(2x + 1)(x - 5)$

Check: outside terms $= (2x)(-5) = -10x$
inside terms $= (1)(x) \quad = \quad \underline{x}$
sum $= \qquad\qquad -9x =$ middle term of original quadratic trinomial

Therefore, factors $(2x + 1)(x - 5)$ are correct.

Alternative method:

$2x^2 - 9x - 5 \qquad\qquad 2 \times -5 = -10$ This is the guide number. It tells you that the two signs are different.

M   A   M

$2x^2 + 1x - 10x - 5$

$x(2x + 1) - 5(2x + 1)$

$(2x + 1)(x - 5)$

M = −10	A = −9
1 × −10 = −10	1 − 10 = −9

exam focus

Some quadratic trinomials can be very challenging to factorise. Do not be discouraged! If you cannot find the correct factors straightaway, keep going until you have tried all options.

4. Difference of two squares

An expression such as $a^2 - b^2$ is called the **difference of two squares**.

> 1. Write each term as a perfect square with brackets.
> 2. Use the rule $a^2 - b^2 = (a - b)(a + b)$.

key point

The difference of two squares is a special case of a trinomial. $x^2 - 25$ can be written as $x^2 + 0x - 25$ and factorised as $(x + 5)(x - 5)$.

Example

Factorise the following:

(i) $x^2 - 16$ 　　　　　　　(ii) $3x^2 - 12y^2$

Solution

(i) $x^2 - 16$

$x^2 - (4)^2$

$(x + 4)(x - 4)$

(ii) $3x^2 - 12y^2$

$3(x^2 - 4y^2)$ 　　　　　(take out common factor)

$3(x^2 - (2y)^2)$

$3(x + 2y)(x - 2y)$

exam Q

Simplify $\dfrac{x^2 + 7x + 12}{x^2 + 2x - 3}$.

Solution

$\dfrac{(x + 3)(x + 4)}{(x + 3)(x - 1)}$ 　　　(factorise the top and bottom)

$\dfrac{x + 4}{x - 1}$ 　　　(divide the top and bottom by $(x + 3)$)

Simplify $\dfrac{5}{2x - 3} - \dfrac{3}{2x^2 - 3x} - \dfrac{1}{x}$.

Solution

$$\dfrac{5}{2x - 3} - \dfrac{3}{x(2x - 3)} - \dfrac{1}{x} \qquad \text{(factorise the denominator)}$$

$$\dfrac{5(x) - 3(1) - 1(2x - 3)}{x(2x - 3)} \qquad \text{(common denominator } x(2x - 3))$$

$$\dfrac{5x - 3 - 2x + 3}{x(2x - 3)}$$

$$\dfrac{3x}{x(2x - 3)} \qquad \text{(divide the top and bottom by } x)$$

$$\dfrac{3}{2x - 3}$$

Changing the subject of a formula

When we rearrange a formula so that one of the variables is given in terms of the others, we are said to be **changing the subject of the formula or manipulating the formulae**. We do this to express one variable in terms of the other variables. The rules in changing the subject of a formula are the same as when solving an equation. That is, we can:

1. **Add** or **subtract** the same quantity to both sides.
2. **Multiply** or **divide** both sides by the same quantity.
3. **Square** both sides, **cube** both sides, etc.
4. Take the **square root** of both sides, take the **cube root** of both sides, etc.

Note: Whatever letter comes after the word 'express' is to be on its own.

Three common **errors** made when manipulating formulae are:

1. $\dfrac{1}{a} + \dfrac{1}{b} \neq \dfrac{1}{a + b}$
2. $\dfrac{a}{b + c} \neq \dfrac{a}{b} + \dfrac{a}{c}$
3. $a\left(\dfrac{b}{c}\right) \neq \dfrac{ab}{ac}$

Example

Rearrange the equation $ab + cd = e$ to make a the subject of the formula.

Solution

$$ab + cd = e$$
$$ab + cd - cd = e - cd \qquad \text{(subtract } cd \text{ from both sides)}$$
$$ab = e - cd$$
$$\frac{ab}{b} = \frac{e - cd}{b} \qquad \text{(divide both sides by } b\text{)}$$
$$a = \frac{e - cd}{b}$$

Example

Temperature can be measured in degrees Celsius or degrees Fahrenheit.
The formula for converting from one to the other is given by $C = \frac{5}{9}(F - 32°)$.
 (i) Rearrange this formula to find F in terms of C.
(ii) Hence, convert 25°C into degrees Fahrenheit.

Solution

(i) $$C = \frac{5}{9}(F - 32°)$$

$$9(C) = 9\left(\frac{5}{9}(F - 32°)\right) \qquad \text{(multiply both sides by 9)}$$

$$9C = 5(F - 32°)$$
$$9C = 5F - 160° \qquad \text{(multiply out the bracket)}$$
$$9C + 160° = 5F \qquad \text{(add 160° to both sides)}$$
$$\frac{9C + 160°}{5} = F \qquad \text{(divide both sides by 5)}$$

(ii) $$F = \frac{9(25°) + 160°}{5} \qquad \text{(let } C = 25°\text{)}$$

$$F = \frac{225° + 160°}{5} = \frac{385°}{5} = 77°$$

Therefore, 25°C = 77°F.

Changing the subject of a formula (manipulating a formula) is an essential skill, which arises in many sections of the course, including area and volume, trigonometry and coordinate geometry.

Example

If $c = \dfrac{b^2 - ac}{b + a}$, express a in terms of the other variables.

Solution

$$c = \frac{b^2 - ac}{b + a}$$

$$(b + a)c = (b + a)\left(\frac{b^2 - ac}{b + a}\right) \qquad \text{(multiply both sides by } (b + a))$$

$$(b + a)c = (b^2 - ac)$$

$$bc + ac = b^2 - ac \qquad \text{(multiply out brackets)}$$

$$ac = b^2 - ac - bc \qquad \text{(subtract } bc \text{ from both sides)}$$

$$ac + ac = b^2 - bc \qquad \text{(add } ac \text{ to both sides)}$$

$$2ac = b^2 - bc$$

$$\frac{2ac}{2c} = \frac{b^2 - bc}{2c} \qquad \text{(divide both sides by } 2c)$$

$$a = \frac{b^2 - bc}{2c}$$

(i) In the study of optical lenses, there is a relationship between the focal length, f, of the lens, the distance the object is placed from the lens, u, and the distance the image is formed from the lens, v. This relationship is expressed as follows: $\frac{1}{f} = \frac{1}{u} + \frac{1}{v}$.

Manipulate this formula to express v in terms of the other variables.

(ii) An object is placed a distance of 20 cm from a lens with a focal length of 15 cm. Find the distance the image is formed from the lens.

Solution

(i)
$$\frac{1}{f} = \frac{1}{u} + \frac{1}{v}$$

$$fuv\left(\frac{1}{f}\right) = fuv\left(\frac{1}{u}\right) + fuv\left(\frac{1}{v}\right) \qquad \text{(multiply each term by the LCM, } fuv\text{)}$$

$$uv = fv + fu$$

$$uv - fv = fv + fu - fv \qquad \text{(subtract } fv \text{ from both sides)}$$

$$uv - fv = fu$$

$$v(u - f) = fu \qquad \text{(factorise out } v\text{)}$$

$$\frac{v(u - f)}{(u - f)} = \frac{fu}{(u - f)} \qquad \text{(divide both sides by } (u - f)\text{)}$$

$$v = \frac{fu}{u - f}$$

(ii) $f = 15$ and $u = 20$:

$$v = \frac{fu}{u - f}$$

$$v = \frac{(15)(20)}{20 - 15} = \frac{300}{5} = 60 \text{ cm}$$

Irrational numbers (surds)

An irrational number is a number which cannot be written in the form $\frac{a}{b}$, where a and b are integers. This means that an irrational number cannot be expressed as a fraction where the numerator and the denominator are whole numbers.

Properties of surds:

1. $\sqrt{ab} = \sqrt{a}\sqrt{b}$ **2.** $\sqrt{\dfrac{a}{b}} = \dfrac{\sqrt{a}}{\sqrt{b}}$ **3.** $\sqrt{a}\sqrt{a} = a$

key point

Simplification of surds

Find the largest possible perfect square number, greater than 1, that will divide evenly into the number under the square root.

Then use the property $\sqrt{ab} = \sqrt{a}\sqrt{b}$.

Remember: perfect squares are 1, 4, 9, 16, 25, 36, 49, . . .

Example

Express each of the following in its simplest surd form:

(i) $\sqrt{27}$ 　　　　(ii) $\dfrac{1}{2}\sqrt{72}$ 　　　　(iii) $\sqrt{2\dfrac{1}{4}}$

Solution

(i) $\sqrt{27} = \sqrt{9 \times 3} = \sqrt{9}\sqrt{3} = 3\sqrt{3}$

(ii) $\dfrac{1}{2}\sqrt{72} = \dfrac{1}{2}\sqrt{36 \times 2} = \dfrac{1}{2}\sqrt{36}\sqrt{2} = \dfrac{1}{2}(6)\sqrt{2} = 3\sqrt{2}$

(iii) $\sqrt{2\dfrac{1}{4}} = \sqrt{\dfrac{9}{4}} = \dfrac{\sqrt{9}}{\sqrt{4}} = \dfrac{3}{2}$

The natural display calculators can be very useful when **verifying** answers to questions on surds.

Addition and subtraction

Surds can be added or subtracted *only* when they have the same irrational parts. If the irrational parts are not the same, reduce each surd to its simplest form, where possible.

Example

Express the following in its simplest surd form: $\sqrt{180} + \sqrt{20} - \sqrt{125}$.

Solution

$\sqrt{180} + \sqrt{20} - \sqrt{125}$

$\sqrt{36 \times 5} + \sqrt{4 \times 5} - \sqrt{25 \times 5}$

$\sqrt{36}\sqrt{5} + \sqrt{4}\sqrt{5} - \sqrt{25}\sqrt{5}$

$6\sqrt{5} + 2\sqrt{5} - 5\sqrt{5}$

$8\sqrt{5} - 5\sqrt{5}$

$3\sqrt{5}$

Addition and subtraction

Express each surd in its simplest form and add or subtract like surds.

e.g. $2\sqrt{a} + 3\sqrt{a} = 5\sqrt{a}$

Multiplication

When multiplying surds, multiply the rational parts by the rational parts and the irrational parts by the irrational parts.

$$a\sqrt{b} \text{ multiplied by } c\sqrt{d} = ac\sqrt{bd}$$

Example

Express the following in its simplest surd form: $3\sqrt{5} \times 2\sqrt{3}$.

Solution

$3\sqrt{5} \times 2\sqrt{3}$

$(3 \times 2) \times (\sqrt{5} \times \sqrt{3})$ (rational parts are 3 and 2, irrational parts are $\sqrt{5}$ and $\sqrt{3}$)

$6\sqrt{15}$

Example

Express the following in its simplest surd form: $2\sqrt{5}(3 + 4\sqrt{5})$.

Solution

$2\sqrt{5}(3 + 4\sqrt{5})$

$6\sqrt{5} + 8\sqrt{25}$

$6\sqrt{5} + 8(5)$

$6\sqrt{5} + 40$

Remember:
$(\sqrt{a})^2 = \sqrt{a} \times \sqrt{a} = a$

Express the following in its simplest surd form: $(2 + 3\sqrt{5})(4 - \sqrt{5})$.

Solution

$(2 + 3\sqrt{5})(4 - \sqrt{5})$

$2(4 - \sqrt{5}) + 3\sqrt{5}(4 - \sqrt{5})$ (use distributive law)

$8 - 2\sqrt{5} + 12\sqrt{5} - 3(5)$ (multiply out brackets)

$8 + 10\sqrt{5} - 15$ (simplify)

$- 7 + 10\sqrt{5}$

Remember the distributive law:
$(A + B)(C + D) = A(C + D) + B(C + D)$

Show that $(2 + \sqrt{7})(2 - \sqrt{7})$ is rational (i.e. not irrational).

Solution

$(2 + \sqrt{7})(2 - \sqrt{7})$

$2(2 - \sqrt{7}) + \sqrt{7}(2 - \sqrt{7})$ (use distributive law)

$4 - 2\sqrt{7} + 2\sqrt{7} - \sqrt{7}(\sqrt{7})$ (multiply out brackets)

$4 - 7$ (note: $(\sqrt{7})(\sqrt{7}) = 7$)

-3

Since there are no surds in the answer, it is rational.

Therefore, $(2 + \sqrt{7})(2 - \sqrt{7})$ is rational.

Let $a = \sqrt{2}$.

(i) For each of the numbers in the table, tick (✓) the correct box to say whether it is *rational* or *irrational*.

Number	Rational	Irrational
a		
$a - 1$		
$(-a)^2$		
$(a - 2)^2$		
$1 + a^2$		

(ii) Show the following numbers on the number line below.

$$a, \quad -a, \quad \sqrt{a}, \quad a^{-2}$$

-2   -1   0   1   2

Solution

(i) To evaluate each element in the table, substitute $a = \sqrt{2}$ into each expression:

$a = \sqrt{2}$ (irrational)

$a - 1 = \sqrt{2} - 1$ (irrational)

$(-a)^2 = (-\sqrt{2})^2 = 2$ (rational)

$(a - 2)^2 = (\sqrt{2} - 2)^2$ (irrational)

$\qquad = (\sqrt{2} - 2)(\sqrt{2} - 2)$

$\qquad = 2 - 2\sqrt{2} - 2\sqrt{2} + 4$

$\qquad = 6 - 4\sqrt{2}$

$1 + a^2 = 1 + (\sqrt{2})^2 = 1 + 2 = 3$ (rational)

Number	Rational	Irrational
a		✓
$a - 1$		✓
$(-a)^2$	✓	
$(a - 2)^2$		✓
$1 + a^2$	✓	

(ii) $a = \sqrt{2} = 1{\cdot}41$ $-a = -\sqrt{2} = -1{\cdot}41$

$\sqrt{a} = \sqrt{(\sqrt{2})} = 1{\cdot}19$ $a^{-2} = \dfrac{1}{a^2} = \dfrac{1}{(\sqrt{2})^2} = \dfrac{1}{2} = 0{\cdot}5$

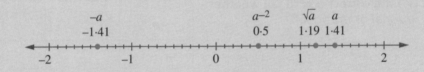

key point

Note that a^{-2} is not a negative number.

2 Solving Equations

☐ To learn how to solve linear equations
☐ To learn how to solve a quadratic equation when given different forms
☐ To be able to apply the methods for solving equations to in-context questions

Solving linear equations

An equation is solved with the following method:

> Whatever you do to one side, you must do **exactly the same** to the other side.

Note: Keep balance in mind.

The solution of an equation is the number that makes both sides balance.

Example

Let $g(x) = 2x - 5$, where $x \in \mathbb{R}$. Find the value of x for which $g(x) = 23$.

Solution

$$g(x) = 2x - 5 \text{ and } g(x) = 23$$

By comparison:

$$23 = 2x - 5$$
$$23 + 5 = 2x \qquad \text{(add 5 to both sides to remove the } -5 \text{ from the RHS)}$$
$$28 = 2x$$
$$14 = x \qquad \text{(divide both sides by 2)}$$

Example

Given that $3a(x + 5) = 114$, find the value of x when $a = 4$.

Solution

$$3a(x + 5) = 114$$
$$3(4)(x + 5) = 114 \qquad \text{(let } a = 4\text{)}$$
$$12(x + 5) = 114$$
$$12x + 60 = 114 \qquad \text{(simplify)}$$
$$12x = 114 - 60 \qquad \text{(subtract 60 from both sides)}$$
$$12x = 54$$
$$x = 4 \cdot 5 \qquad \text{(divide both sides by 12)}$$

A plumber charges €90 for a service call. If the service call exceeds 60 minutes in duration the plumber charges an additional €1·25 for every minute over the first 60 minutes. If the bill for a plumbing repair job was €125, how many minutes did the service call take?

Solution

Let n = number of minutes of the call.

Then $(n - 60)$ is the number of additional minutes after the first 60 minutes of the service call.

Form an equation:

service charge + €1·25 per additional minute = cost of the service call

$$90 + 1 \cdot 25(n - 60) = 125$$
$$90 + 1 \cdot 25n - 75 = 125 \qquad \text{(simplify)}$$
$$15 + 1 \cdot 25n = 125$$
$$1 \cdot 25n = 110 \qquad \text{(subtract 15 from both sides)}$$
$$n = 88 \qquad \text{(divide both sides by 1·25)}$$

Therefore, the plumber spent 88 minutes doing the service call.

A goldsmith combined pure gold that costs €5·20 per gram with 50 g of a gold alloy that costs €2·80 per gram. How many grams of the pure gold were used to make an alloy of gold that costs €4·40 a gram?

Solution

Let x = number of grams of pure gold.

Form an equation:

€5·20 (grams of pure gold)
 + €2·80(grams of gold alloy) = €4.40 (total grams of pure gold + alloy of gold)

$$€5{\cdot}20(x) + €2{\cdot}80(50) = €4{\cdot}40(x + 50)$$
$$€5{\cdot}20(x) + €140 = €4{\cdot}40(x) + €220$$
$$€5{\cdot}20(x) - €4{\cdot}40(x) = €220 - €140$$
$$€0{\cdot}80(x) = €80$$
$$x = 100$$

Therefore, 100 g of pure gold was added.

A landscaping company is contracted to install a sprinkler system into each home in a new housing development in Spain. For each system installed, the landscape company calculates that it will need the following supplies:

Twelve 10-metre PVC pipes

Nine sprinkler heads

1 set of miscellaneous PVC parts

The project manager decides that he should also order 15 extra 10-metre PVC pipes, 6 extra sprinkler heads and 2 extra sets of miscellaneous PVC parts.

Each 10-metre PVC pipe costs €1·50, each sprinkler head costs €2·50 and each set of PVC parts costs €15.

 (i) Calculate the total cost of one sprinkler system and hence write an equation for the total the landscape company will pay for the supplies needed to install sprinkler systems into a garden.

 (ii) If the company installs 12 sprinkler systems, how much will it cost for supplies?

 (iii) If the manager budgets €6,006 for the entire project, how many sprinkler systems can be installed?

Solution

 (i) Each sprinkler system needs: Twelve 10-metre PVC = 12(1·50) = €18·00

Nine sprinkler heads = 9(2·50) = €22·50

One bag of PVC pieces = €15·00

Cost per sprinkler system = €55·50

Additional supplies: 15 10-metre PVC = 15(1·50) = €22·50

6 sprinkler heads = 6(2·50) = €15·00

2 bags of PVC pieces = 2(15) = €30·00

Cost per sprinkler system = €67·50

The total cost for n gardens:

Total cost = (cost per sprinkler system)(number of gardens)
            + (additional supplies)

Total cost = €55·50(n) + €67·50

(ii) Total cost for 12 sprinkler systems:

$$\text{Total cost} = €55·50(n) + €67·50$$
$$= €55·50(12) + €67·50 \qquad (\text{let } n = 12)$$
$$= €666 + €67·50$$
$$\text{Total cost} = €733·50$$

(iii) Based on a budget of €6,006:

$$\text{Total cost} = €55·50(n) + €67·50$$
$$€6,006 = €55·50(n) + €67·50$$
$$€5,938·50 = €55·50(n) \qquad (\text{subtract €67·50 from both sides})$$
$$107 = n \qquad (\text{divide both sides by 107})$$

Therefore, with a budget of €6,006, the company can install 107 sprinkler systems.

Linear equations with fractions

If there are fractions in an equation, multiply all parts by a number that all of the denominators divide evenly into. This number is known as the common denominator.

Example

Solve the equation $\dfrac{1}{2}(7x - 2) + 5 = 2x + 7$.

Solution

$$\frac{1}{2}(7x - 2) + 5 = 2x + 7$$

$$2\left(\frac{1}{2}(7x - 2)\right) + 2(5) = 2(2x) + 2(7) \qquad (\text{multiply each term by 2})$$

$$1(7x - 2) + 2(5) = 2(2x) + 2(7) \qquad (\text{divide the denominators into the LCM})$$

$$7x - 2 + 10 = 4x + 14 \qquad (\text{multiply out brackets})$$

$$7x + 8 = 4x + 14 \qquad (\text{simplify})$$

$$7x - 4x = 14 - 8 \qquad (\text{rearrange})$$

$$3x = 6 \qquad (\text{simplify})$$

$$x = 2 \qquad (\text{divide both sides by 3})$$

Solve the equation $\dfrac{x-7}{2} = \dfrac{x+3}{6}$.

Solution

$$\dfrac{x-7}{2} = \dfrac{x+3}{6}$$

$$\cancel{6}\left(\dfrac{x-7}{\cancel{2}}\right) = \cancel{6}\left(\dfrac{x+3}{\cancel{6}}\right)$$ (multiply each term by the LCM 6)

$$3(x-7) = 1(x+3)$$ (divide the denominators into the LCM)

$$3x - 21 = x + 3$$ (multiply out brackets)

$$3x - x = 3 + 21$$ (rearrange)

$$2x = 24$$ (simplify)

$$x = 12$$ (divide both sides by 2)

Solve the equation $\dfrac{3(x+3)}{4} - \dfrac{2(x-3)}{3} = \dfrac{x+1}{2}$.

Solution

$$\dfrac{3(x+3)}{4} - \dfrac{2(x-3)}{3} = \dfrac{x+1}{2}$$ (the LCM of 4, 3 and 2 is 12)

$$\cancel{12}\left(\dfrac{3(x+3)}{4}\right) - \cancel{12}\left(\dfrac{2(x-3)}{3}\right) = \cancel{12}\left(\dfrac{x+1}{2}\right)$$ (multiply each term by 12)

$$3(3(x+3)) - 4(2(x-3)) = 6(x+1)$$ (divide the denominators into the LCM)

$$9(x+3) - 8(x-3) = 6(x+1)$$

$$9x + 27 - 8x + 24 = 6x + 6$$ (multiply out brackets)

$$x + 51 = 6x + 6$$ (simplify)

$$51 - 6 = 6x - x$$ (rearrange)

$$45 = 5x$$ (divide both sides by 5)

$$9 = x$$

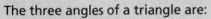

The three angles of a triangle are:

$$\frac{8(x-2)}{3}, \ 4x+7, \ \frac{5x-10}{2}.$$

Find the value of x.

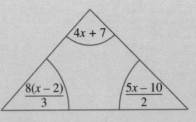

Solution

The three angles of a triangle sum to 180°.

$$\left(\frac{8(x-2)}{3}\right) + (4x+7) + \left(\frac{5x-10}{2}\right) = 180$$

$$6\left(\frac{8(x-2)}{3}\right) + 6(4x+7) + 6\left(\frac{5x-10}{2}\right) = 6(180) \qquad \text{(multiply each term by 6)}$$

$$2(8(x-2)) + 6(4x+7) + 3(5x-10) = 6(180) \qquad \text{(divide the denominators into the LCM)}$$

$$16(x-2) + 24x + 42 + 15x - 30 = 1{,}080 \qquad \text{(multiply out brackets)}$$

$$16x - 32 + 39x + 12 = 1{,}080 \qquad \text{(simplify)}$$

$$55x - 20 = 1{,}080$$

$$55x = 1{,}100 \qquad \text{(add 20 to both sides)}$$

$$x = 20 \qquad \text{(divide both sides by 55)}$$

exam focus

Notice the link between geometry and algebra in this question.

Quadratic equations

Any equation of the form $ax^2 + bx + c = 0$, $a \neq 0$, is called a quadratic equation. Solving a quadratic equation gives us the roots of the equation. These are the two values which satify the equation.

To solve a quadratic equation you must factorise the expression, let each factor equal zero and solve. Methods of factorising were covered in Chapter 1.

key point

It is vital for you to remember and be very familiar with the following types of factorising:

Take out common terms	Difference of two squares	Factorise a trinomial
$x^2 + 2x = x(x + 2)$	$x^2 - 9 = (x + 3)(x - 3)$	$x^2 + 6x - 7 = (x - 1)(x + 7)$

Example

Solve the following quadratic equations:

(i) $2x^2 + 6x = 0$ (ii) $x^2 - 64 = 0$

Solution

(i)
$$2x^2 + 6x = 0$$
$$2x(x + 3) = 0 \quad \text{(factorise)}$$
$$2x = 0 \quad \text{or} \quad x + 3 = 0$$
$$x = 0 \quad \text{or} \quad x = -3 \text{ (solve)}$$

(ii)
$$x^2 - 64 = 0$$
$$(x + 8)(x - 8) = 0 \quad \text{(factorise)}$$
$$x + 8 = 0 \quad \text{or} \quad x - 8 = 0$$
$$x = -8 \quad \text{or} \quad x = 8 \text{ (solve)}$$

Example

Solve the following quadratic equations:

(i) $x^2 + 2x - 15 = 0$ (ii) $2x^2 + x - 10 = 0$

Solution

(i)
$$x^2 + 2x - 15 = 0$$
$$(x + 5)(x - 3) = 0 \quad \text{(factorise)}$$
$$x + 5 = 0 \quad \text{or} \quad x - 3 = 0$$
$$x = -5 \quad \text{or} \quad x = 3 \text{ (solve)}$$

(ii)
$$2x^2 + x - 10 = 0$$
$$(2x + 5)(x - 2) = 0 \quad \text{(factorise)}$$
$$2x + 5 = 0 \quad \text{or} \quad x - 2 = 0$$
$$2x = -5 \quad \text{or} \quad x = 2 \text{ (solve)}$$
$$x = \frac{-5}{2} \quad \text{or} \quad x = 2$$

exam focus

The application of solving quadratic equations appears throughout your course. You must know this very well.

exam Q

(i) Factorise $x^2 + 4x + 4$.

(ii) Simplify $\sqrt{x^2 + 4x + 4} + \sqrt{x^2 + 2x + 1}$, given that $x \geq 0$.

(iii) Given that $x \geq 0$, solve for x: $\sqrt{x^2 + 4x + 4} + \sqrt{x^2 + 2x + 1} = x^2$.

Solution

(i) $x^2 + 4x + 4$

$(x + 2)(x + 2)$ 　　　(factorise)

$(x + 2)^2$

(ii) $\sqrt{x^2 + 4x + 4} + \sqrt{x^2 + 2x + 1}$

$\sqrt{(x + 2)(x + 2)} + \sqrt{(x + 1)(x + 1)}$ 　(factorise each quadratic)

$\sqrt{(x + 2)^2} + \sqrt{(x + 1)^2}$

$(x + 2) + (x + 1)$ 　　　　　　　(a square and a square root cancel each other)

$x + 2 + x + 1$ 　　　　　　　　(remove brackets)

$2x + 3$ 　　　　　　　　　　　(simplify)

(iii) $\sqrt{x^2 + 4x + 4} + \sqrt{x^2 + 2x + 1} = x^2$

　　　　　　　　$2x + 3 = x^2$ 　　　(from part (ii))

　　　　　　　　$0 = x^2 - 2x - 3$

　　　　　　　　$0 = (x - 3)(x + 1)$

　　　　　$x - 3 = 0$ 　or　 $x + 1 = 0$

　　　　　　$x = 3$ 　　or　　 $x = -1$ （Reject since $x \geq 0$）

Constructing a quadratic equation when given its roots

Forming a quadratic equation is the opposite process to solving:

1. Let x equal each root.
2. Form the factors.
3. Multiply the factors by each other to form the equation.

key point

An alternative, and quicker, way to form a quadratic equation when given its roots is:

$$x^2 - (\text{sum of roots})x + (\text{product of roots}) = 0$$

Example

Form the quadratic equation with roots -2 and 4.

Solution

Roots -2 and 4

Let $x = -2$ and $x = 4$.

$x + 2 = 0$ and $x - 4 = 0$ (form the factors)

$(x + 2)(x - 4) = 0$

$x^2 + 2x - 4x - 8 = 0$ (multiply the factors)

$x^2 - 2x - 8 = 0$ (simplify)

Alternative method: find the sum of the roots and the product of the roots.

Sum of roots $= -2 + 4 = 2$ Product of the roots $= (-2)(4) = -8$

$x^2 - (\text{sum of roots})x + (\text{product of roots}) = 0$

$x^2 - (2)x + (-8) = 0$

$x^2 - 2x - 8 = 0$

Quadratic formula

In many quadratic equations, $ax^2 + bx + c$ cannot be resolved into factors. When this happens, the formula **must** be used.

A clue that you must use the formula is often given in the question. When the question requires an approximate answer, e.g. 'correct to two decimal places', 'correct to three significant figures', 'correct to the nearest integer' or 'express your answer in surd form', then the formula must be used.

The roots of the quadratic equation $ax^2 + bx + c = 0$ are given by the formula

$$x = \frac{-b \pm \sqrt{b^2 - 4ac}}{2a}.$$

Notes: 1. The entire top line on the right-hand side, including $-b$, is divided by $2a$.

2. It is often called the quadratic formula or the $-b$ formula.

3. Before using the formula, make sure every term is on the left-hand side of the equation, i.e. write the equation in the form $ax^2 + bx + c = 0$.

(see the booklet of formulae and tables, page 20)

Example

Solve the following quadratic equations.

(i) $3x^2 - 5x - 13 = 0$, leaving your answer correct to one decimal place.

(ii) $2x^2 - 7x + 4 = 0$, leaving your answer in surd form.

Solution

(i) $3x^2 - 5x - 13 = 0$

$$x = \frac{-b \pm \sqrt{b^2 - 4ac}}{2a}$$ $a = 3, b = -5, c = -13$

$$= \frac{-(-5) \pm \sqrt{(-5)^2 - 4(3)(-13)}}{2(3)}$$

We are asked to leave the answers to one decimal place, so we know that we must use the formula.

$$= \frac{5 \pm \sqrt{25 + 156}}{6}$$

$$= \frac{5 \pm \sqrt{181}}{6}$$

Therefore, $x = \dfrac{5 + \sqrt{181}}{6} = 3{\cdot}1$ or $x = \dfrac{5 - \sqrt{181}}{6} = -1{\cdot}4$

(ii) $2x^2 - 7x + 4 = 0$ $a = 2, b = -7, c = 4$

$$x = \frac{-b \pm \sqrt{b^2 - 4ac}}{2a}$$

We are asked to leave the answers in surd form, so we know that we must use the formula.

$$= \frac{-(-7) \pm \sqrt{(-7)^2 - 4(2)(4)}}{2(2)}$$

$$= \frac{7 \pm \sqrt{49 - 32}}{4}$$

$$= \frac{7 \pm \sqrt{17}}{4}$$

Take care when b is a negative value.
$-b = -(-7) = +7$

Therefore, $x = \dfrac{7 + \sqrt{17}}{4}$ or $x = \dfrac{7 - \sqrt{17}}{4}$.

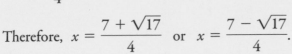

Verify that $3 - \sqrt{2}$ is a root (solution) of the equation $x^2 - 6x + 7 = 0$.

Solution

Solve the quadratic equation and see if one of the roots is $3 - \sqrt{2}$.

$$x^2 - 6x + 7 = 0$$

$$x = \frac{-b \pm \sqrt{b^2 - 4ac}}{2a} \qquad a = 1, b = -6, c = 7$$

$$= \frac{-(-6) \pm \sqrt{(-6)^2 - 4(1)(7)}}{2(1)}$$

$$= \frac{6 \pm \sqrt{36 - 28}}{2}$$

$$= \frac{6 \pm \sqrt{8}}{2}$$

$$= \frac{6 \pm 2\sqrt{2}}{2}$$

> **key point**
>
> We can also verify a root by substituting it into the equation. If it satisfies the equation (i.e. the left side equals the right side), then it is a root. Otherwise it is not.

$$= 3 \pm \sqrt{2}$$

$$x = 3 + \sqrt{2} \text{ or } x = 3 - \sqrt{2}$$

Thus, we have verified that $3 - \sqrt{2}$ is a root of the equation $x^2 - 6x + 7 = 0$.

A diver jumps from a platform that is 10 m high. The height of the diver above the water t seconds after jumping is modelled by:

$$h = -4 \cdot 9t^2 + 3 \cdot 2t + 10 \cdot 5.$$

(i) Find the height of the diver after 1·5 seconds.

(ii) Find, to the nearest hundredth of a second, how long after jumping it will take for the diver to hit the water.

Solution

(i) Find the height, h, when $t = 1 \cdot 5$ seconds:

$$h = -4 \cdot 9t^2 + 3 \cdot 2t + 10 \cdot 5$$

$$= -4 \cdot 9(1 \cdot 5)^2 + 3 \cdot 2(1 \cdot 5) + 10 \cdot 5$$

$$= -11 \cdot 025 + 4 \cdot 8 + 10 \cdot 5$$

$$= 4 \cdot 275 \text{ m}$$

> **exam focus**
>
> Write down what values you have and what you want in terms of the variables used.

Therefore, the diver is 4·275 m above the water after 1·5 seconds.

(ii) When the diver hits the water, his height is 0 m. Thus, we need to find t when $h = 0$.

$$h = -4 \cdot 9t^2 + 3 \cdot 2t + 10 \cdot 5$$

$$0 = -4 \cdot 9t^2 + 3 \cdot 2t + 10 \cdot 5$$

Use the quadratic formula, where $a = -4 \cdot 9$, $b = 3 \cdot 2$ and $c = 10 \cdot 5$.

$$t = \frac{-b \pm \sqrt{b^2 - 4ac}}{2a}$$

$$= \frac{-(3 \cdot 2) \pm \sqrt{(3 \cdot 2)^2 - 4(-4 \cdot 9)(10 \cdot 5)}}{2(-4 \cdot 9)}$$

$$= \frac{-3 \cdot 2 \pm \sqrt{10 \cdot 24 + 205 \cdot 8}}{-9 \cdot 8}$$

$$= \frac{-3 \cdot 2 \pm \sqrt{216 \cdot 04}}{-9 \cdot 8}$$

$$\therefore \quad t = \frac{-3 \cdot 2 + \sqrt{216 \cdot 04}}{-9 \cdot 8} \quad \text{or} \quad t = \frac{-3 \cdot 2 - \sqrt{216 \cdot 04}}{-9 \cdot 8}$$

$$t = -1 \cdot 1733 \qquad\qquad\qquad t = 1 \cdot 82636$$

He jumped at $t = 0$ sec, so the solution cannot be a negative value.

Therefore, the time to hit the water is $1 \cdot 83$ sec to the nearest one-hundredth of a second.

A rectangular piece of cardboard has a length which is 8 cm more than its width, w. An open box is formed by cutting squares, whose side are 2 cm in length, from each corner of the rectangular piece of card, then folding up the sides.

(i) Write the dimensions of the box in terms of w.

(ii) Find the dimensions of the box if its volume is 256 cm³.

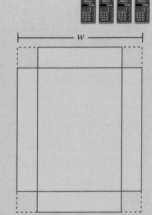

Solution

(i) Width of cardboard $= w$

Length of cardboard $= w + 8$ (length is 8 cm more than the width)

Width of box $= w - 4$ (width minus 2 cm on each end)

Length of box $= w + 8 - 4 = w + 4$ (length minus 2 cm from each end)

Height of box $= 2$

(ii) Dimensions of the box are:

Width $= w - 4$, length $= w + 4$, height $= 2$

Volume $= $ (length)(width)(height)   (formula must be known)

$256 = (w + 4)(w - 4)(2)$

$256 = (w^2 - 4w + 4w - 16)(2)$

$256 = (w^2 - 16)(2)$

$256 = 2w^2 - 32$

$0 = 2w^2 - 288$ (divide both sides by 2)

$0 = w^2 - 144$

$0 = (w + 12)(w - 12)$ (factorise)

$w + 12 = 0$ or $w - 12 = 0$

     $w = -12$ or $w = 12$

Reject $w = -12$, as lengths must always be positive.

Therefore, the dimensions of the box are:

width $= w - 4 = 8$ cm,   length $= w + 4 = 16$ cm and height $= 2$ cm.

exam focus

The last example involves nets from the topic of area and volume. If you get more than one answer it is important for you to look at which solutions make sense. Apply logic to determine which answers, if any, to reject.

Quadratic equations involving fractions

Use the common denominator to rewrite the equation by multiplying all parts by the common denominator. Then factorise and solve the resulting quadratic equation.

Example

(i) Solve: $\dfrac{1}{x + 1} + \dfrac{4}{2x - 1} = \dfrac{5}{3}$.

(ii) Verify the integer solution.

Solution

(i) Multiply each part by the common denominator: $(x + 1)(2x - 1)(3)$.

$$(\cancel{x + 1})(2x - 1)(3)\left(\frac{1}{\cancel{x + 1}}\right)$$

$$+ (x + 1)(\cancel{2x - 1})(3)\left(\frac{4}{\cancel{2x - 1}}\right) = (x + 1)(2x - 1)(\cancel{3})\left(\frac{5}{\cancel{3}}\right)$$

$$(2x - 1)(3)(1) + (x + 1)(3)(4) = (x + 1)(2x - 1)(5)$$

$$(2x - 1)(3) + (x + 1)(12) = (x + 1)(10x - 5)$$
$$6x - 3 + 12x + 12 = 10x^2 - 5x + 10x - 5$$
$$18x + 9 = 10x^2 + 5x - 5$$
$$0 = 10x^2 - 13x - 14$$
$$0 = (10x + 7)(x - 2)$$
$$10x + 7 = 0 \qquad x - 2 = 0$$
$$x = -\frac{7}{10} \qquad x = 2$$

(ii) $x = 2$ is the integer solution, therefore substitute $x = 2$ into:

$$\frac{1}{x + 1} + \frac{4}{2x - 1} = \frac{5}{3}$$

$$\frac{1}{2 + 1} + \frac{4}{2(2) - 1} = \frac{5}{3}$$

$$\frac{1}{3} + \frac{4}{4 - 1} = \frac{5}{3}$$

$$\frac{1}{3} + \frac{4}{3} = \frac{5}{3}$$

$$\frac{5}{3} = \frac{5}{3}$$

Since the left-hand side equals the right-hand side, we have verified $x = 2$ as a solution.

When substituting a solution into an equation, if LHS = RHS the solution satisfies the equation.

Example

Solve the equation $\dfrac{2}{3x - 4} - \dfrac{1}{2x + 1} = \dfrac{1}{2}$ and give your answer correct to one decimal place.

Solution

Multiply each part by the common denominator: $(3x - 4)(2x + 1)(2)$

$$(3x - 4)(2x + 1)(2)\left(\frac{2}{3x - 4}\right)$$

$$- (3x - 4)(2x + 1)(2)\left(\frac{1}{2x + 1}\right) = (3x - 4)(2x + 1)(2)\left(\frac{1}{2}\right)$$

$$(2x + 1)(2)(2) - (3x - 4)(2)(1) = (3x - 4)(2x + 1)(1)$$

$$(2x + 1)(4) - (3x - 4)(2) = (3x - 4)(2x + 1)$$
$$(8x + 4) - (6x - 8) = 6x^2 + 3x - 8x - 4$$
$$8x + 4 - 6x + 8 = 6x^2 - 5x - 4$$
$$2x + 12 = 6x^2 - 5x - 4$$
$$0 = 6x^2 - 7x - 16$$

We are asked to leave the answers to one decimal place, so we know that we must use the quadratic formula:

$$x = \frac{-b \pm \sqrt{b^2 - 4ac}}{2a} \qquad a = 6, b = -7, c = -16$$

$$= \frac{-(-7) \pm \sqrt{(-7)^2 - 4(6)(-16)}}{2(6)}$$

$$= \frac{7 \pm \sqrt{49 + 384}}{12}$$

$$= \frac{7 \pm \sqrt{433}}{12}$$

Therefore, $x = \dfrac{7 + \sqrt{433}}{12} = 2{\cdot}3$ or $x = \dfrac{7 - \sqrt{433}}{12} = -1{\cdot}2.$

exam Q

A resistor is an electrical component which reduces the current flowing through a circuit. The resistance of these resistors is measured in units called ohms and resistance is always a positive value. Two resistors are placed in parallel, as in the diagram. One resistor is 3 ohm greater than the other resistor. Their total effective resistance (R_T) is found to be 2 ohm.

Calculate the value of each resistor, given that the formula for calculating the total resistance is:

R_1

R_2

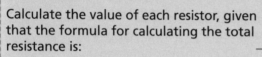
$$\frac{1}{R_T} = \frac{1}{R_1} + \frac{1}{R_2}$$

Solution

One resistor is 3 ohms **greater** than the other resistor. This means that if one resistor has a resistance of R, then the other resistor has a resistance of $R + 3$.

Let   resistor 1 $(R_1) = R$,   resistor 2 $(R_2) = R + 3$,   total resistance $(R_T) = 2$.

$$\frac{1}{R_T} = \frac{1}{R_1} + \frac{1}{R_2}$$

$$\frac{1}{2} = \frac{1}{R} + \frac{1}{R + 3} \quad \text{(multiply all parts by } 2(R)(R + 3))$$

$$(2)(R)(R + 3)\left(\frac{1}{2}\right) = (2)(R)(R + 3)\left(\frac{1}{R}\right) + (2)(R)(R + 3)\left(\frac{1}{R + 3}\right)$$

$$(R)(R + 3)(1) = (2)(R + 3)(1) + (2)(R)(1)$$

$$R^2 + 3R = 2R + 6 + 2R$$

$$R^2 - R - 6 = 0$$

$$(R - 3)(R + 2) = 0$$

$$R = 3 \quad \text{or} \quad R = -2$$

Reject $R = -2$, as you can't have a negative resistance.

Therefore, resistance of $R_1 = 3$ ohm, resistance of $R_2 = 6$ ohm.

To solve problems which involve real-life situations, draw a diagram, if possible. Write the problem in the form of an algebraic equation. Manipulate the equation and solve.

Sadhbh cycled from Ennis to Limerick, a distance of 30 km. She left Ennis at 11:20 and arrived in Limerick at 13:10, having stopped in Bunratty for a 20-minute break. Bunratty is 22 km from Ennis.

(i) Sadhbh's average speed between Ennis and Bunratty was x km/h. Write an expression in x to complete this part of her journey.

(ii) Her average speed for the second part of her journey, between Bunratty and Limerick, was 6 km/h slower than her speed between Ennis and Bunratty. Write an expression in x for the time it took to complete the second part of her journey.

(iii) Write an equation in x to represent the above information.

(iv) Solve the equation to find Sadhbh's speed for each part of the journey.

Solution

(i) Speed $= x$, distance $= 22$ km

$$\text{Time} = \frac{\text{Distance}}{\text{Speed}}$$

$$T_1 = \frac{22}{x} \qquad \text{(time in hours)}$$

(ii) Her speed for the second part of the trip was 6 km/h slower than her speed for the first part. Therefore, speed $= x - 6$.

Speed $= x - 6$, distance $= 8$ km

$$\text{Time} = \frac{\text{Distance}}{\text{Speed}}$$

$$T_2 = \frac{8}{x - 6} \qquad \text{(time in hours)}$$

Remember the formulae which relate distance, speed and time:

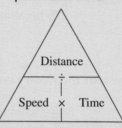

(iii) Total time $= (11{:}20 \rightarrow 13{:}10) - 20\text{-minute break}$

$$= 1 \text{ hr } 50 \text{ minutes} - 20\text{-minute break}$$

$$= 1 \text{ hr } 30 \text{ minutes}$$

$$= 1{\cdot}5 \text{ hours} = \frac{3}{2} \text{ hours}$$

Total time $= T_1 + T_2$

$$\frac{3}{2} = \frac{22}{x} + \frac{8}{x - 6}$$

(iv) Solve the equation:

$$\frac{3}{2} = \frac{22}{x} + \frac{8}{x - 6} \qquad \text{(mulitply all parts by } (2)(x)(x - 6))$$

$$(2)(x)(x - 6)\left(\frac{3}{2}\right) = (2)(x)(x - 6)\left(\frac{22}{x}\right) + (2)(x)(x - 6)\left(\frac{8}{x - 6}\right)$$

$$(x^2 - 6x)(3) = (x - 6)(44) + (x)(16)$$

$$3x^2 - 18x = 44x - 264 + 16x$$

$$3x^2 - 18x = 60x - 264$$

$$3x^2 - 78x + 264 = 0$$

$$x^2 - 26x + 88 = 0$$

$$(x - 22)(x - 4) = 0$$

$$x - 22 = 0 \quad \text{or} \quad x - 4 = 0$$

$$x = 22 \quad \text{or} \quad x = 4$$

$x \neq 4$, as x must be bigger than 6.

Therefore, $x = 22$ is the only acceptable solution.

Therefore, speed between Ennis and Bunratty: $x = 22$ km/h

speed between Bunratty and Limerick: $x - 6 = 16$ km/h

3 Inequalities

☐ To learn how to solve linear inequalities
☐ To learn how to graph a solution set on a number line
☐ To be able to apply inequality methods to in-context questions

The four inequality symbols are:

1. $>$ means greater than   **2.** $\geq$ means greater than or equal to
3. $<$ means less than   **4.** $\leq$ means less than or equal to

Algebraic expressions that are linked by one of the four inequality symbols are called **inequalities**. For example, $3x - 1 \geq 11$ and $-3 < 2x - 1 \leq 7$ are inequalities.

Solving inequalities is exactly the same as solving equations, with the following exception:

key point

Multiplying or dividing both sides of an inequality by a **negative** number **reverses** the direction of the inequality symbol.

That is:

$>$ changes to $<$ $\geq$ changes to $\leq$
$<$ changes to $>$ $\leq$ changes to $\geq$

Solving an inequality means finding the values of x that make the inequality true. The following rules apply to graphing inequalities on a number line:

Number line for $x \in \mathbb{N}$ or $x \in \mathbb{Z}$, use dots.

Number line for $x \in \mathbb{R}$, use a full heavy line.

Note: Inequalities can be turned around. For example:

$5 \leq x$ means the same as $x \geq 5$
$8 \geq x \geq 3$ means the same as $3 \leq x \leq 8$

(see booklet of formulae and tables, page 23)

It is vital that you are familiar with the basic **number systems:**

$\mathbb{N} = \{1, 2, 3, \ldots\}$, the set of natural numbers.

$\mathbb{Z} = \{\ldots -2, -1, 0, 1, 2, \ldots\}$, the set of integers.

$\mathbb{R} =$ all whole numbers, decimals, rational and irrational numbers, known as the set of real numbers.

Inequalities in one variable

Example

Find the solution set of $11 - 3x \geq 2$, $x \in \mathbb{N}$ and graph your solution on the number line.

Solution

$11 - 3x \geq 2$

$\quad -3x \geq -9$ (subtract 11 from both sides)

$\quad\ 3x \leq 9$ (multiply both sides by -1 and reverse the direction of the inequality)

$\quad\ x \leq 3$ (divide both sides by 3)

As $x \in \mathbb{N}$, this is the set of natural numbers less than or equal to 3.

Thus, the values of x are 1, 2 and 3.

Number line:

Note: As $x \in \mathbb{N}$, dots are used on the number line.

Example

Find the range of values of $x \in \mathbb{R}$ for which $4(x - 2) > 5(2x - 1) - 9$ and graph your solution on the number line.

Solution

$4(x - 2) > 5(2x - 1) - 9$

$\quad 4x - 8 > 10x - 5 - 9$ (remove the brackets)

$4x - 10x > -5 - 9 + 8$ (rearrange)

$\quad\quad -6x > -6$ (simplify both sides)

$\quad\quad\ 6x < 6$ (multiply both sides by -1 and reverse the inequality, i.e. turn $>$ into $<$)

$\quad\quad\ x < 1$ (divide both sides by 6)

Number line:

```
←——+————+————+————+————⊕————+————→
   -3       -2       -1        0        1        2
```

Notes: 1. As $x \in \mathbb{R}$, we use full heavy shading on the number line.

key point

2. A circle is put around 1 to indicate that it is **not** included in the solution.

> The inequality is $<$ and not $\leq$, so you must put a hollow circle on the number line and not a dot.

Example

(i) Find the solution set A of $2x + 7 \leq 11, x \in \mathbb{R}$.

(ii) Find the solution set B of $4 - 2x < 10, x \in \mathbb{R}$.

(iii) Find $A \cap B$ and graph your solution on the number line.

Solution

We solve each inequality separately and then combine the solutions.

(i) A: $2x + 7 \leq 11$
$$2x \leq 4$$
$$x \leq 2$$

(ii) B: $4 - 2x < 10$
$$-2x < 6$$
$$2x > -6$$
$$x > -3$$

(iii) Combining the two inequalities gives:

$$A \cap B: \quad -3 < x \leq 2, \quad x \in \mathbb{R}$$

This is the set of positive and negative whole numbers between -3 and 2, including 2 but not including -3.

Number line:

```
←——+————+————⊕————+————+————+————+————•————+————→
   -4       -3       -2       -1        0        1        2        3
```

Notes: 1. As $x \in \mathbb{R}$, we use full heavy shading on the number line.

2. A hollow circle is put around -3 to indicate that it is **not** included in the solution.

3. A dot is drawn on 2 to indicate it is included in the solution.

exam focus

Students often have difficulty determining the correct region for the final answer. Spend some time practising this.

(i) Find A, the solution set of $3x - 5 < 7$, $x \in \mathbb{Z}$.

(ii) Find B, the solution set of $\dfrac{-2 - 3x}{4} \leq 1$, $x \in \mathbb{Z}$.

(iii) List the elements of $A \cap B$.

Solution

(i) $3x - 5 < 7$

$\quad\quad 3x < 7 + 5$ \quad\quad (add 5 to both sides)

$\quad\quad 3x < 12$

$\quad\quad x < 4$ \quad\quad (divide both sides by 3)

Therefore, set A contains all integers less than 4.

$A = \{3, 2, 1, 0, -1, -2, -3, -4 \ldots\}$

(ii) $\quad \dfrac{-2 - 3x}{4} \leq 1$

$\quad 4\left(\dfrac{-2 - 3x}{4}\right) \leq 4(1)$ \quad\quad (multiply both sides by 4)

$\quad\quad -2 - 3x \leq 4$

$\quad\quad -2 - 4 \leq 3x$

$\quad\quad -6 \leq 3x$

$\quad\quad -2 \leq x$ \quad (divide both sides by 3)

Therefore, set B contains all integers greater than or equal to -2.

$B = \{-2, -1, 0, 1, 2, 3, 4, 5, 6, \ldots\}$

(iii) To find $A \cap B$ we must combine the two inequalities: $A \cap B = -2 \leq x < 4$.

Therefore, the elements of $A \cap B$ are $\{-2, -1, 0, 1, 2, 3\}$.

Claire calls A1 Towing to tow her car after it broke down. A1 towing charges €75 to cover the call out fee and towing for the first 10 kilometres. They then charge €3·00 for each additional kilometre towed. Let k be the number of kilometres towed over 10 km.

(i) Claire can afford to spend no more than €115 to tow her car. Write an inequality in terms of k to represent this information.

(ii) Solve the inequality from **(i)** and hence find the total maximum number of whole kilometres Claire can get her car towed.

Solution

(i) (call out charge) + (charge per km over 10 km) ≤ 115

$$(75) + (3k) \leq 115$$

(ii) $(75) + (3k) \leq 115$

$$3k \leq 115 - 75$$
$$3k \leq 40$$
$$k \leq 13 \cdot 333333$$

Therefore, Claire can get her car towed 13 km over the 10 km, so she can get her car towed a total distance of 23 km.

Solve the following inequality. Show the solution set on a number line.

$$5 - \frac{3}{4}x \leq \frac{19}{8}, \qquad x \in \mathbb{R}$$

Solution

$$5 - \frac{3}{4}x \leq \frac{19}{8}$$

$$8(5) - 8\left(\frac{3}{4}x\right) \leq 8\left(\frac{19}{8}\right) \qquad \text{(multiply all parts by 8)}$$

$$40 - 6x \leq 19$$

$$-6x \leq 19 - 40 \qquad \text{(subtract 40 from both sides)}$$

$$-6x \leq -21$$

$$x \geq 3 \cdot 5 \qquad \text{(divide both sides by } -6 \text{ and reverse the}$$
$$\text{inequality, i.e. turn } \leq \text{ into } \geq)$$

Number line:

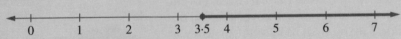

Notes: 1. As $x \in \mathbb{R}$, we use full heavy shading on the number line.

       2. A dot is put at 3·5 to indicate that it is included in the solution.

The width of a rectangle is x cm and its length is $(2x - 3)$ cm, where $x \in \mathbb{N}$.

(i) If the perimeter of the rectangle must be greater than 30 cm, find the smallest possible value of x.

(ii) Hence, find the area of the rectangle for this value of x.

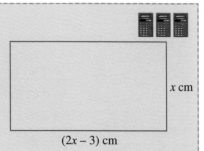

x cm

$(2x - 3)$ cm

Solution

(i)
$$\text{Perimeter} > 30$$
$$2(\text{length}) + 2(\text{width}) > 30$$
$$2(2x - 3) + 2(x) > 30$$
$$4x - 6 + 2x > 30$$
$$6x - 6 > 30$$
$$6x > 36$$
$$x > 6$$

Therefore, the smallest possible value of x is 7 cm, since $x \in \mathbb{N}$.

(ii) If $x = 7$:

Width = 7 and length = $2(7) - 3 = 11$

Area = length $\times$ width

Area = 7×11

Area = 77 cm^2

Double inequalities

A double inequality is one like $-3 \leq 5x + 2 \leq 7$.

There are two methods for solving double inequalities.

Method 1:

> Whatever we do to one part, we do the same to all three parts.

Method 2:

> 1. Write the double inequality as two separate simple inequalities.
> 2. Solve each simple inequality and combine their solutions.

Example

Solve $-4 \leq 3x + 2 < 11$, $x \in \mathbb{R}$.

Solution

Method 1: Do the same to all three parts.

$$-4 \leq 3x + 2 < 11$$
$$-6 \leq 3x < 9 \qquad \text{(subtract 2 from each part)}$$
$$-2 \leq x < 3 \qquad \text{(divide each part by 3)}$$

Method 2: Write the double inequality as two separate simple inequalities.

2nd inequality

$$-4 \leq 3x + 2 < 11$$

1st inequality

$$-4 \leq 3x + 2 \quad \text{and} \quad 3x + 2 < 11$$
$$-6 \leq 3x \qquad\qquad\qquad 3x < 9$$
$$-2 \leq x \qquad\qquad\qquad\quad x < 3$$

$$-2 \leq x < 3 \qquad\qquad \text{(combining solutions)}$$

This means that the value for x is greater than or equal to -2 and less than 3.

Number line:

(number line from -3 to 4, with a filled dot at -2 and a hollow circle at 3, heavy shading between)

Notes: 1. As $x \in \mathbb{R}$, we use full heavy shading on the number line.
2. A hollow circle is put around 3 to indicate that 3 is **not** included in the solution.
3. A dot is put on -2 to indicate that -2 is part of the solution.

exam Q

The relationship between Celsius temperature and Fahrenheit temp-erature is given by the formula $F = \dfrac{9}{5}C + 32$. If the temperature in New York City on a certain day is between 77°F and 86°F, what is the temperature range in degrees Celsius?

Solution

$$77 < F < 86 \qquad\qquad \text{Let } F = \dfrac{9}{5}C + 32$$

$$77 < \dfrac{9}{5}C + 32 < 86$$

$$385 < 9C + 160 < 430 \qquad \text{(multiply all parts by 5)}$$
$$225 < \quad 9C \quad < 270 \qquad \text{(subtract 160 from each part)}$$
$$25 < \quad C \quad < 30 \qquad \text{(divide all parts by 9)}$$

Therefore, the temperature is between 25°C and 30°C.

Hence the temperature range $= 5°C$

exam focus

The above solution uses method 1 for solving. You should be aware that using method 2 would result in the same answer.

In the triangle ABC, |AC| is 1 cm longer than |AB|. |BC| is 2 cm longer than |AB|. Find, to the nearest whole number, the possible values for |AB| if the perimeter of △ABC is more than 15cm but less than 25 cm.

Solution

Let |AB| = x.

Then: |AC| = x + 1

|BC| = x + 2

15 < perimeter < 25

15 < (x) + (x + 1) + (x + 2) < 25   (perimeter = sum of three sides)

15 < x + x + 1 + x + 2 < 25

15 < 3x + 3 < 25

12 < 3x < 22   (subtract 3 from each part)

4 < x < 7·33   (divide all parts by 3)

Therefore, |AB| can be 5 cm, 6 cm or 7 cm in length.

In a college course a student can achieve a distinction, a merit, a pass or a fail.

A distinction is awarded for a mean result of 80% to 100%.

A merit is awarded for a mean result of 60% to 80% (not including 80%).

A pass is awarded for a mean result of 40% to 60% (not including 60%).

A mean of less than 40% is deemed to be a fail.

Dominic has scores of 74%, 73%, 77% and 81% on his first four exams.

(i) Find the range of percentages that Dominic must get on the fifth exam to ensure that he is awarded a merit.

(ii) Find the range of percentages that Dominic must get on the fifth exam to ensure that he is awarded a distinction.

(iii) Based on your answers from (i) and (ii), which do you think is more likely: that Dominic will be awarded a merit or a distinction on this course? Give a reason for your answer.

Solution

(i) Mean score = $\dfrac{74 + 73 + 77 + 81 + x}{5} = \dfrac{305 + x}{5}$

To achieve a merit: Mean score must be 60% to 80% (not including 80%).

$$60 \leq \text{mean score} < 80 \qquad \text{(mean must be less than 80\%)}$$

$$60 \leq \dfrac{305 + x}{5} < 80$$

$$300 \leq 305 + x < 400 \qquad \text{(multiply all parts by 5)}$$

$$300 - 305 \leq x < 400 - 305 \qquad \text{(subtract 305 from all parts)}$$

$$-5 \leq x < 95$$

Therefore, Dominic must obtain a percentage between −5% and 95%. However, the lowest percentage possible is 0%. Thus, if Dominic scores a result between 0% and 95% (not including 95%), he will earn a merit.

(ii) To achieve a distinction: Mean score must be 80% to 100%.

$$80 \leq \text{mean score} \leq 100$$

$$80 \leq \dfrac{305 + x}{5} \leq 100$$

$$400 \leq 305 + x < 500 \qquad \text{(multiply all parts by 5)}$$

$$400 - 305 \leq x < 500 - 305 \qquad \text{(subtract 305 from all parts)}$$

$$95 \leq x < 195$$

Therefore, Dominic must obtain a percentage between 95% and 195%. However, the highest percentage possible is 100%. Thus, if Dominic scores a result between 95% and 100%, he will earn a distinction.

key point

It is important for you to apply logic to this question. You must realise that Dominic cannot score a result below 0% or above 100%, so dismiss those options.

(iii) The highest result that Dominic has scored so far on any of the other exams is 81%. In order for Dominic to obtain a distinction he must get 95% or higher. Therefore, in my opinion it would be very unlikely that Dominic will get a result high enough to earn a distinction. Thus, I think it is most likely that Dominic will be awarded a merit on this course.

exam focus

This question incorporates aspects of statistics and probability. These are topics which we usually associate with Paper 2. It is important for you to be aware that any topics can appear on either paper.

4 Simultaneous Equations

☐ To learn how to use suitable strategies for finding solutions to:
  o Simultaneous linear equations with two unknowns
  o. One linear equation and one quadratic equation with two unknowns
☐ To learn how to interpret the results from solving two equations simultaneously

Simultaneous linear equations with two unknowns

Simultaneous linear equations in two variables are solved with the following steps.

1. Write both equations in the form $ax + by = k$ and label the equations ① and ②.
2. Multiply one or both of the equations by a number in order to make the coefficients of x or y the same, but of opposite sign.
3. Add to remove the variable with equal coefficients but of opposite sign.
4. Solve the resultant equation to find the value of the remaining unknown (x or y).
5. Substitute this value into equation ① and ② to find the value of the other unknown.

Solution containing fractions
If the answer at step 4 is a fraction, the substitution might be difficult. In such cases, you can repeat steps 1 to 4 for the other variable.

Example

Solve the following pair of simultaneous equations:

$$2x + 3y = 5$$

$$x - 4y = -14$$

Solution

To eliminate the y:

$$2x + 3y = 5 \quad (\times 4)$$

$$\underline{x - 4y = -14 \quad (\times 3)}$$

$$8x + 12y = 20$$

$$\underline{3x - 12y = -42 \quad \text{(add the rows)}}$$

$$11x = -22 \quad (\div 11)$$

$$x = -2$$

Therefore, the solution is $x = -2, y = 3$.

To find the value for y, let $x = -2$ in either of the equations:

$$2x + 3y = 5$$

$$2(-2) + 3y = 5$$

$$-4 + 3y = 5$$

$$3y = 9$$

$$y = 3$$

Example

Let the cost of a meal for an adult be €x and the cost of a meal for a child be €y. The cost of a meal for 3 adults and 2 children amounts to €125. The cost of a meal for 2 adults and 3 children amounts to €115.

(i) Write down two equations in x and y to represent this information.

(ii) Solve these equations to find the cost of an adult's meal and the cost of a child's meal.

Solution

(i) The cost of a meal for 3 adults and 2 children amounts to €125: $3x + 2y = 125$.

The cost of a meal for 2 adults and 3 children amounts to €115: $2x + 3y = 115$.

(ii) Solving simultaneously:

$$3x + 2y = 125 \quad (\times -3)$$

$$\underline{2x + 3y = 115 \quad (\times 2)}$$

$$-9x - 6y = -375$$

$$\underline{4x + 6y = 230}$$

$$-5x \quad = -145 \quad (\div -5)$$

$$x = 29$$

Substitute $x = 29$ into one of the equations:

$$3(29) + 2y = 125$$

$$87 + 2y = 125$$

$$2y = 125 - 87$$

$$2y = 38$$

$$y = 19$$

Therefore, an adult meal costs €29 and a child's meal costs €19.

Example

Solve the equations for p and q:

$$\frac{2p - 5}{3} + \frac{q}{5} = 6; \qquad\qquad \frac{3p}{10} + 2 = \frac{3q - 5}{2}$$

Solution

Equation ①: $\qquad \dfrac{2p - 5}{3} + \dfrac{q}{5} = 6 \qquad\qquad (\times 15)$

$$5(2p - 5) + 3(q) = 15(6)$$
$$10p - 25 + 3q = 90$$
$$10p + 3q = 115 \qquad ①$$

Equation ②: $\qquad \dfrac{3p}{10} + 2 = \dfrac{3q - 5}{2} \qquad\qquad (\times 10)$

$$1(3p) + 10(2) = 5(3q - 5)$$
$$3p + 20 = 15q - 25$$
$$3p - 15q = -45 \qquad ②$$

Now solve ① and ②: $\quad 10p + 3q = 115 \qquad\qquad (\times 5)$

$$\underline{\quad 3p - 15q = -45 \quad}$$
$$50p + 15q = 575$$
$$\underline{\quad 3p - 15q = -45 \quad}$$
$$53p = 530 \qquad\qquad (\div 53)$$
$$p = 10$$

Sub $p = 10$ into ①: $\quad 10(10) + 3q = 115$

$$100 + 3q = 115$$
$$3q = 15 \qquad\qquad (\div 5)$$
$$q = 5$$

Answer: $p = 10$ and $q = 5$.

key point

Equations do not always have to be in terms of x and y.

The image shows two lines, *l* and *k*, graphed on the coordinated plane.

(i) Use the graph to estimate the point of intersection of the two lines.

(ii) By observation or otherwise, write down the equation of each of the lines in the form $y = mx + c$.

(iii) Solve these equations simultaneously to find the point of intersection. Give your answer to two significant figures.

(iv) The point of intersection can be found either by reading the graph or using algebra. State one advantage of finding the point of intersection using algebra.

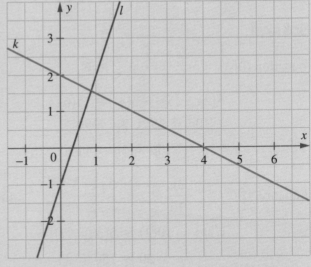

Solution

(i) Estimated point of intersection: (0·8, 1·6).

(ii) To express equations in the form of $y = mx + c$, we need to find the slope of the line and the point where it crosses the *y*-axis (*y*-intercept).

Line *l*:   Slope $= m = \dfrac{3}{1} = 3$ *y*-intercept, $c = -1$

∴ $l : y = 3x - 1$

Line *k*: Slope $= m = \dfrac{-2}{4} = -\dfrac{1}{2}$ *y*-intercept, $c = 2$

∴ $k : y = -\dfrac{1}{2}x + 2$

key point

$\text{slope} = \dfrac{\text{rise}}{\text{run}}$

(iii) Equation *l*: $y = 3x - 1$

Equation *k*: $y = -\dfrac{1}{2}x + 2$

Let $y = y$: $\Rightarrow 3x - 1 = -\dfrac{1}{2}x + 2$

$6x - 2 = -x + 4$ (multiply all parts by 2)

$6x + x = 4 + 2$

$7x = 6$

$x = \dfrac{6}{7} \Rightarrow x = 0{\cdot}857$

Substitute $x = \dfrac{6}{7}$ into equation *l*: $\quad y = 3x - 1$

$$y = 3\left(\frac{6}{7}\right) - 1 \quad (\times 7)$$

$$7y = 18 - 7$$

$$7y = 11$$

The answer does not have to be an integer.

$$y = \frac{11}{7} \Rightarrow y = 1.571$$

Thus, the point of intersection to two significant figures = (0.86, 1.6).

(iv) Using algebra to find the point of intersection gives a more accurate solution.

It is very important when solving simultaneous equations to maintain total concentration. If you make a mistake near the start of the solution, you may have difficulty getting an answer and waste valuable exam time.

One linear equation and one quadratic equation with two unknowns

Before you can solve a pair of linear and quadratic equations, it is important for you to recognise which equation is the linear one and which is the quadratic one.

Linear equation
The highest exponent of each term is 1,
e.g. $2x + y - 8 = 0$.

Quadratic equation
The highest exponent, or the sum of the exponents, of any term is 2,
e.g. $x^2 + xy + y^2 = 5$.

To solve one linear equation and one quadratic equation with two unknowns, use the following steps.

1. From the linear equation, express one variable in terms of the other.
2. Substitute this into the quadratic equation and solve.
3. Substitute separately the value(s) obtained in step 2 into the linear equation in step 1 to find the corresponding value(s) of the other variable.

Example

Solve the following pair of equations:

$$2x + y = 3$$
$$x^2 + xy + y^2 = 3$$

Solution

Rearrange the linear equation to get y on its own: $y = 3 - 2x$.

Substitute $y = 3 - 2x$ into the quadratic equation:

$$x^2 + xy + y^2 = 3$$

Substitute the values for x into the linear equation to find values for y:

$$x^2 + x(3 - 2x) + (3 - 2x)^2 = 3$$
$$x^2 + 3x - 2x^2 + 9 - 12x + 4x^2 = 3$$
$$3x^2 - 9x + 9 = 3$$
$$3x^2 - 9x + 6 = 0$$
$$x^2 - 3x + 2 = 0$$
$$(x - 1)(x - 2) = 0$$

$x - 1 = 0$ or $x - 2 = 0$

$x = 1$ or $x = 2$

$x = 1$	$x = 2$
$y = 3 - 2x$	$y = 3 - 2x$
$y = 3 - 2(1)$	$y = 3 - 2(2)$
$y = 3 - 2$	$y = 3 - 4$
$y = 1$	$y = -1$

Ans: $x = 1, y = 1$ Ans: $x = 2, y = -1$

exam
Q

The diagram shows the curve $y = 17 - 2x - x^2$ and the line $x + y = 5$.

(i) Find their points of intersections, A and B.

(ii) Hence, find the coordinates of the points C and D, where lines parallel to the y-axis through A and B cross the x-axis.

(iii) Find the area of the trapezium $ABCD$.

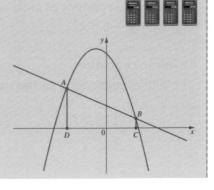

Solution

(i) Rearrange the equation for the line to get y on its own: $y = 5 - x$.

Substitute $y = 5 - x$ into the quadratic equation:

$$y = 17 - 2x - x^2$$
$$5 - x = 17 - 2x - x^2$$
$$x^2 + 2x - 17 + 5 - x = 0$$
$$x^2 + x - 12 = 0$$
$$(x + 4)(x - 3) = 0$$
$$x + 4 = 0 \quad \text{or} \quad x - 3 = 0$$
$$x = -4 \quad \text{or} \quad x = 3$$

Substitute the values for x into the linear equation to find values for y:

$x = -4$	$x = 3$
$y = 5 - x$	$y = 5 - x$
$y = 5 - (-4)$	$y = 5 - (3)$
$y = 5 + 4$	$y = 5 - 3$
$y = 9$	$y = 2$
$A = (-4, 9)$	$B = (3, 2)$

(ii) The points C and D are vertically beneath the points B and A, respectively. This means they will have the same x-coordinates as A and B. Since C and D are on the x-axis, their y-coordinates are zero. Therefore, $C = (3, 0)$ and $D = (-4, 0)$.

(iii) Use the coordinates of the vertices to find the length of the sides of the trapezium.

$$\text{Area} = \left(\frac{a + b}{2}\right)h \quad \text{(see booklet of formulae and tables, page 8)}$$

Where a and b are the parallel sides.

$$\text{Area} = \left(\frac{9 + 2}{2}\right)(7)$$

$$\text{Area} = \left(\frac{11}{2}\right)(7)$$

$$\text{Area} = (5 \cdot 5)(7)$$

$$\text{Area} = 38 \cdot 5 \text{ sq. units}$$

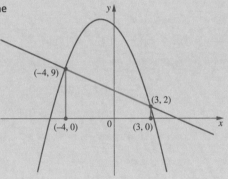

exam focus

The previous exam question is a good example of links between different topics. In this case algebra and area.

An asteroid belt follows a pattern that is modelled by the equation:

$$3x^2 + y^2 - 13x - 7y = 0.$$

A rocket is on a linear path that can be modelled by the equation: $y = x$.

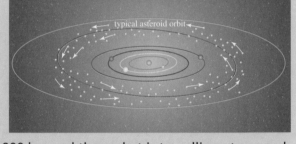

typical asteroid orbit

(i) Find the two points where the rocket enters and leaves the asteroid belt.

(ii) One unit is equivalent to 15,000 km and the rocket is travelling at a speed of 30,000 km/h. Find the time it takes from when the rocket enters the asteroid belt until it leaves on the far side.

Solution

(i) Substitute $y = x$ into the quadratic equation:

Substitute the values for x into the linear equation to find values for y:

$$3x^2 + y^2 - 13x - 7y = 0$$
$$3x^2 + (x)^2 - 13x - 7(x) = 0$$
$$3x^2 + x^2 - 13x - 7(x) = 0$$
$$4x^2 - 20x = 0$$
$$4x(x - 5) = 0$$

$$4x = 0 \text{ and } x - 5 = 0$$
$$x = 0 \text{ and } \quad x = 5$$

$x = 0$	$x = 5$
$y = x$	$y = x$
$y = 0$	$y = 5$
$(0, 0)$	$(5, 5)$

Therefore, the rocket enters and leaves the asteroid belt at the points $(0, 0)$ and $(5, 5)$.

(ii) The rocket enters at the point $(0, 0)$ and leaves at $(5, 5)$ (or vice versa).

Find the distance between the points where the rocket enters and leaves the asteroid belt.

$(0, 0) = (x_1, y_1)$ Distance $= \sqrt{(x_2 - x_1)^2 + (y_2 - y_1)^2}$ (See booklet of formulae and tables, page 18)

$(5, 5) = (x_2, y_2)$ Distance $= \sqrt{(5 - 0)^2 + (5 - 0)^2}$

$$= \sqrt{25 + 25}$$
$$= \sqrt{50} \text{ units}$$

Distance through the asteroid belt $= \sqrt{50} \times 15{,}000 \text{ km} = 106{,}066 \text{ km}$

$$\text{Time} = \frac{\text{Distance}}{\text{Speed}} = \frac{10{,}6066}{30{,}000} = 3 \cdot 54$$

Therefore, it takes the rocket $3 \cdot 54$ hours to pass through the asteroid belt.

aims

- To become familiar with the rules of indices
- To learn how to use the rules of indices to solve problems
- To understand index notation
- To be able to work with index notation when solving problems

In the expression a^m, a is the base and m is the index.

The index can also be called the power or the exponent.

key point

a^m is read as 'a to the power of m'.

Rules of Indices

(see booklet of tables and formule, page 21)

Where $a, b \in \mathbb{R}$; $p, q \in \mathbb{Q}$; $a, b \neq 0$:

Rule	Example	
1. $a^p a^q = a^{p+q}$	$5^4 5^3 = 5^{4+3} = 5^7$	$x^3 x^5 = x^{3+5} = x^8$
2. $\dfrac{a^p}{a^q} = a^{p-q}$	$\dfrac{3^5}{3^2} = 3^{5-2} = 3^3$	$\dfrac{x^7}{x^3} = x^{7-3} = x^4$
3. $(a^p)^q = a^{pq}$	$(3^2)^4 = 3^8$	$(x^3)^4 = x^{12}$
4. $a^0 = 1$	$7^0 = 1$	$x^0 = 1$
5. $a^{-p} = \dfrac{1}{a^p}$	$4^{-2} = \dfrac{1}{4^2}$ or $5^3 = \dfrac{1}{5^{-3}}$	$x^{-3} = \dfrac{1}{x^3}$ or $x^2 = \dfrac{1}{x^{-2}}$
6. $a^{\frac{1}{q}} = \sqrt[q]{a}$ $\quad q \in \mathbb{Z}, q \neq 0, a > 0$	$5^{\frac{1}{3}} = \sqrt[3]{5}$	$x^{\frac{1}{5}} = \sqrt[5]{x}$
7. $a^{\frac{p}{q}} = \sqrt[q]{a^p} = (\sqrt[q]{a})^p$ $\quad p, q \in \mathbb{Z}, q \neq 0, a > 0$	$9^{\frac{2}{3}} = \sqrt[3]{9^2} = (\sqrt[3]{9})^2$	$x^{\frac{2}{5}} = \sqrt[5]{x^2} = (\sqrt[5]{x})^2$
8. $(ab)^p = a^p b^p$	$(2x)^3 = 2^3 x^3 = 8x^3$	$(xy)^5 = x^5 y^5$
9. $\left(\dfrac{a}{b}\right)^p = \dfrac{a^p}{b^p}$	$\left(\dfrac{3}{5}\right)^2 = \dfrac{3^2}{5^2} = \dfrac{9}{25}$	$\left(\dfrac{x}{y}\right)^3 = \dfrac{x^3}{y^3}$

exam Q

Write the following without using indices.

(i) 6^{-2} **(ii)** $81^{\frac{1}{2}}$

Solution

(i) $6^{-2} = \dfrac{1}{6^2} = \dfrac{1}{36}$ **(ii)** $81^{\frac{1}{2}} = \sqrt{81} = 9$

exam focus

You could use your natural display calculator to **verify** these expressions. You can only use your calculator when the base number is a constant and not a variable. Make sure you are familiar with all the functions on your calculator.

Example

Simplify each of the following.

(i) $(a^3 \times a^4)^2$ **(ii)** $125^{\frac{2}{3}}$ **(iii)** $32^{\frac{2}{5}} - 81^{\frac{1}{4}}$

Solution

(i) $(a^3 \times a^4)^2$ **(ii)** $125^{\frac{2}{3}}$ **(iii)** $32^{\frac{2}{5}} - 81^{\frac{1}{4}}$

$(a^{3+4})^2$ $\sqrt[3]{125^2}$ $\sqrt[5]{32^2} - \sqrt[4]{81^1}$

$(a^7)^2$ $(\sqrt[3]{125})^2$ $(\sqrt[5]{32})^2 - \sqrt[4]{81}$

$a^{7 \times 2}$ 5^2 $2^2 - 3$

a^{14} 25 $4 - 3$

                                                         1

exam Q

Show that $\dfrac{(a\sqrt{a})^3}{a^4}$ simplifies to $\sqrt{a}$.

Solution

$\dfrac{(a\sqrt{a})^3}{a^4}$

$= \dfrac{\left(a\left(a^{\frac{1}{2}}\right)\right)^3}{a^4}$ (since $\sqrt{a} = a^{\frac{1}{2}}$)

$= \dfrac{\left(a^{1+\frac{1}{2}}\right)^3}{a^4}$ (using the rule $a^p a^q = a^{p+q}$)

$= \dfrac{\left(a^{\frac{3}{2}}\right)^3}{a^4}$

$= \dfrac{a^{\frac{9}{2}}}{a^4}$ (using the rule $(a^p)^q = a^{pq}$

$= a^{\frac{9}{2}-4}$ (using the rule $\dfrac{a^p}{a^q} = a^{p-q}$)

$= a^{\frac{1}{2}}$

$= \sqrt{a}$

This exam question was impossible to complete without using several of the rules of indices. It is vital that you are very familiar with these rules.

Therefore, $\dfrac{(a\sqrt{a})^3}{a^4}$ simplifies to $\sqrt{a}$.

exam Q

(i) Express b in terms of a and c where $\dfrac{8a - 5b}{b} = c$.

(ii) Hence or otherwise, evaluate b when $a = 3^3$ and $c = 2^4$.

Solution

(i) $\dfrac{8a - 5b}{b} = c$

$b\left(\dfrac{8a - 5b}{b}\right) = b(c)$ (multiply both sides by b)

$8a - 5b = bc$

$$8a = bc + 5b \quad \text{(add } 5b \text{ to both sides)}$$
$$8a = b(c + 5) \quad \text{(factorise out } b\text{)}$$
$$\frac{8a}{c + 5} = b \quad \text{(divide both sides by } (c + 5)\text{)}$$

(ii) Let $a = 3^3$ and $c = 2^4$:

$$\frac{8a}{c + 5} = b$$

$$\frac{8(3^3)}{2^4 + 5} = b$$

$$\frac{8(27)}{16 + 5} = b$$

$$\frac{216}{21} = b$$

$$\frac{72}{7} = b$$

'Hence or otherwise' means you should try to use your answers from part (i).

Simplify $\dfrac{x^5 \times x^2 \times \sqrt[3]{x^2}}{x^3 \times x^{\frac{4}{3}}}$, giving your answer in the form $x^{\frac{a}{b}}$, $a,\, b \in \mathbb{Z}$.

Solution

$$\frac{x^5 \times x^2 \times \sqrt[3]{x^2}}{x^3 \times x^{\frac{4}{3}}}$$

$$\frac{x^5 \times x^2 \times x^{\frac{2}{3}}}{x^3 \times x^{\frac{4}{3}}} \qquad \left(\text{use the rule: } a^{\frac{p}{q}} = \sqrt[q]{a^p}\right)$$

$$\frac{x^{5+2+\frac{2}{3}}}{x^{3+\frac{4}{3}}} \qquad \left(\text{use the rule: } a^p a^q = a^{p+q}\right)$$

$$\frac{x^{\frac{23}{3}}}{x^{\frac{13}{3}}} \qquad \text{(simplify powers)}$$

$$x^{\frac{23}{3} - \frac{13}{3}} \qquad \left(\text{use the rule: } \frac{a^p}{a^q} = a^{p-q}\right)$$

$$x^{\frac{10}{3}}$$

Exponential equations

An equation involving the variable in the power is called an **exponential equation**. Exponential equations are solved with the following steps.

1. Write all the numbers as powers of the same number (usually a prime number).
2. Write both sides as one power of the same number, using the laws of indices.
3. Equate these powers and solve the equation.

Example

Find the value of x for which $2^{x+3} = 4^x$.

Solution

$2^{x+3} = 4^x$

$2^{x+3} = (2^2)^x$ (write 4 as a power of 2)

$2^{x+3} = 2^{2x}$

$x + 3 = 2x$ (equate powers)

$3 = 2x - x$ (subtract x from both sides)

$3 = x$

Find the value of x for which $49^x = 7^{2+x}$ and verify your answer.

Solution

$49^x = 7^{2+x}$

$(7^2)^x = 7^{2+x}$ (write 49 as a power of 7)

$7^{2x} = 7^{2+x}$

$2x = 2 + x$ (equate powers)

$2x - x = 2$ (subtract x from both sides)

$x = 2$

Verify $x = 2$ in the equation: $49^x = 7^{2+x}$

$49^2 = 7^{2+2}$

$49^2 = 7^4$

$2,401 = 2,401$

Since the left side equals the right side, $x = 2$ satisfies the equation and so is verified as a solution.

Example

Solve for x in each of the following equations.

(i) $27^{4+3x} = 243^{1+2x}$

(ii) $2^{x^2} = 8^{2x+9}$

Solution

(i) $27^{4+3x} = 243^{1+2x}$

$(3^3)^{4+3x} = (3^5)^{1+2x}$

$3^{12+9x} = 3^{5+10x}$

$12 + 9x = 5 + 10x$ (equate powers)

$7 = x$

(ii)

$2^{x^2} = 8^{2x+9}$

$2^{x^2} = (2^3)^{2x+9}$

$2^{x^2} = 2^{6x+27}$

$x^2 = 6x + 27$ (equate powers)

$x^2 - 6x - 27 = 0$

$(x - 9)(x + 3) = 0$

$x - 9 = 0$ or $x + 3 = 0$

$x = 9$ or $x = -3$

Factorising was essential in solving part (ii) in the previous question. Factorising is a vital skill to have throughout your entire maths course. Factorising was covered in Chapter 1. Spend time on this.

(i) Find the value of 3^6.

(ii) Write 27 in the form 3^k, where $k \in \mathbb{N}$.

(iii) Find the value of x for which $27 \times 3^x = \dfrac{1}{729}$.

Solution

(i) Use you calculator to find: $3^6 = 729$ (ii) $27 = 3^3$

(iii) $27 \times 3^x = \dfrac{1}{729}$

$3^3 \times 3^x = \dfrac{1}{3^6}$ (using (i) and (ii))

$3^{3+x} = 3^{-6}$

$3 + x = -6$ (equate powers)

$x = -6 - 3$

$x = -9$

exam Q

(i) Evaluate $27^{\frac{1}{3}}$.

(ii) Express $9^{\frac{1}{4}}$ in the form 3^k, $k \in \mathbb{Q}$.

(iii) Solve for x the equation $\left(27^{\frac{1}{3}}\right)\left(9^{\frac{1}{4}}\right) = 3^{4-x}$.

Solution

(i) $27^{\frac{1}{3}} = \sqrt[3]{27} = 3$

(ii) $9^{\frac{1}{4}} = (3^2)^{\frac{1}{4}} = 3^{\frac{1}{2}}$

(iii) $\left(27^{\frac{1}{3}}\right)\left(9^{\frac{1}{4}}\right) = 3^{4-x}$

$(3)\left(3^{\frac{1}{2}}\right) = 3^{4-x}$ (sub in from (i) and (ii))

$3^{1+\frac{1}{2}} = 3^{4-x}$

$3^{\frac{3}{2}} = 3^{4-x}$

$\dfrac{3}{2} = 4 - x$ (equate the powers)

$3 = 8 - 2x$ (multiply all parts by 2)

$2x = 8 - 3$

$2x = 5$

$x = 2 \cdot 5$ (divide both parts by 2)

---

exam Q

Solve for x and y: $2^x = 8^{y+1}$

$3^{x-9} = 9^y$

Solution

$2^x = 8^{y+1}$

$2^x = (2^3)^{y+1}$

$2^x = 2^{3y+3}$

$x = 3y + 3$

$x - 3y = 3$ ①

$3^{x-9} = 9^y$

$3^{x-9} = (3^2)^y$

$3^{x-9} = 3^{2y}$

$x - 9 = 2y$

$x - 2y = 9$ ②

Use simultaneous equations to solve:

$x - 3y = 3$ ① $(x - 1)$

$x - 2y = 9$ ②

$-x + 3y = -3$

$x - 2y = 9$

$y = 6$

Substitute $y = 6$ into ①:

$x - 3y = 3$

$x - 3(6) = 3$

$x - 18 = 3$

$x = 21$

$x = 21$ and $y = 6$

The number of bacteria on a kitchen counter can be estimated with the model

$$B(n) = 45(2^n)$$

where $B(n)$ is the number of bacteria after n 20-minute intervals.

(i) Use the model to estimate the number of bacteria present after 1 hour.

(ii) Use the model to estimate the number of bacteria present after 4 hours.

(iii) Use the model to find how long it will be until there are 1,440 bacteria.

Solution

(i) One hour = three 20-minute intervals, so let $n = 3$: $B(n) = 45(2^n)$

$$B(3) = 45(2^3)$$
$$B(3) = 360$$

Therefore, there will be 360 bacteria present after one hour.

(ii) Four hours = twelve 20-minute intervals, so let $n = 12$: $B(n) = 45(2^n)$

$$B(12) = 45(2^{12})$$
$$B(12) = 184{,}320$$

Therefore, there will be 184,320 bacteria present after four hours.

(iii) To find the time taken for 1,440 bacteria to be present: find n when $B(n) = 1{,}440$:

$$B(n) = 45(2^n)$$
$$1{,}440 = 45(2^n) \quad \text{(let } B(n) = 1{,}440)$$
$$32 = 2^n \quad \text{(divide both sides by 45)}$$
$$2^5 = 2^n \quad \text{(let } 32 = 2^5)$$
$$5 = n \quad \text{(equate powers)}$$

There will be 1,440 bacteria present after five 20-minute intervals.

Thus, after 1 hour 40 minutes, there will be 1,440 bacteria present.

Statistics indicate that the world population since World War II has been growing exponentially. The world population can be modeled by $P(t) = 4(1 \cdot 019)^t$ where $P(t)$ is the world population in billions and t is the time in years since 1975.

(i) Use the formula to estimate the world population, in billions, in 1995, correct to two decimal places.

(ii) Use the formula to estimate the world population, in billions, in 2020, correct to two decimal places.

Solution

(i) The number of years between 1995 and 1975: $1995 - 1975 = 20$ years.
So, we must find the population when $t = 20$:

$$P(t) = 4(1 \cdot 019)^t$$
$$P(20) = 4(1 \cdot 019)^{20} \quad \text{(let } t = 20)$$
$$P(20) = 5 \cdot 828323799 \quad \text{(using calculator)}$$

Therefore, the world population in 1995 was estimated to be 5·83 billion.

(ii) The number of years between 2020 and 1975: $2020 - 1975 = 45$ years.
So, we must find the population when $t = 45$:

$$P(t) = 4(1 \cdot 019)^t$$
$$P(45) = 4(1 \cdot 019)^{45} \quad \text{(let } t = 45)$$
$$P(45) = 9 \cdot 33 \quad \text{(using calculator)}$$

Therefore, the world population in 2020 was estimated to be 9·33 billion.

There are more questions of this type in the chapters on pattern and the chapter on arithmetic.

Index notation

When dealing with very large or very small numbers it can be easier to perform calculations if the numbers are expressed in the form $a \times 10^n$, where $1 \leq a < 10$ and $n \in \mathbb{Z}$.

It is crucial that you know how to put your calculator into scientific mode and be able to enter data that is in index notation.

CASIO	SHARP
Put your calculator into scientific mode:	Put your calculator into scientific mode:
SHIFT + SETUP	Set up
7 : Sci	1 : FSE
	1 : SCI
Select a number between 0 and 9. This is the number of significant figures the calculator will display. Selecting 9 will be fine.	Select a number between 0 and 9. This is the number of significant figures the calculator will display. Selecting 9 will be fine.
To enter $6 \cdot 7 \times 10^{-15}$	To enter $6 \cdot 7 \times 10^{-15}$
press the following buttons:	press the following buttons:
$\boxed{6}\,\boxed{\cdot}\,\boxed{7}\,\boxed{\times 10^x}\,\boxed{(-)}\,\boxed{1}\,\boxed{5}$	$\boxed{6}\,\boxed{\cdot}\,\boxed{7}\,\boxed{\text{Exp}}\,\boxed{(-)}\,\boxed{1}\,\boxed{5}$

Express 2^{24} in the form $a \times 10^n$, where $1 \le a < 10$ and $n \in \mathbb{N}$, correct to three significant figures.

Solution

Put your calculator into scientific mode.

Enter 2^{24} and press the equal button:

$$1\cdot6777216 \times 10^7$$

$$1\cdot6800000 \times 10^7 \qquad \text{(to three significant figures)}$$

$$1\cdot68 \times 10^7$$

Example

Simplify $\dfrac{(2\cdot4 \times 10^{13}) \times (1\cdot8 \times 10^{-4})}{3\cdot5 \times 10^3}$, using your calculator.

Solution

Start by putting your calculator into scientific mode.

$$\frac{(2\cdot4 \times 10^{13}) \times (1\cdot8 \times 10^{-4})}{3\cdot5 \times 10^3}$$

$$= \frac{4\cdot32 \times 10^9}{3\cdot5 \times 10^3} \qquad \text{(use your calculator to simplify the top)}$$

$$= 1\cdot23428571 \times 10^6 \qquad \text{(use your calculator to simplify the fraction)}$$

(i) The number $2^{61} - 1$ is a prime number. Using your calculator or otherwise, express its value, correct to two significant figures, in the form $a \times 10^n$, where $1 \le a < 10$ and $n \in \mathbb{N}$.

(ii) Use your answer to part (i) to state how many digits there are in the exact value of $2^{61} - 1$.

Solution

(i) Put your calculator into scientific mode.
Enter $2^{61} - 1$ and press the equal button:

$$2 \cdot 305843009 \times 10^{18}$$

$$2 \cdot 300000000 \times 10^{18} \quad \text{(to two significant figures)}$$

$$2 \cdot 3 \times 10^{18}$$

(ii) From **(i)**, $2^{61} - 1 = 2 \cdot 3 \times 10^{18}$

$2 \cdot 3 \times 10^{18}$ means there are 18 numbers **after** the decimal point.

Therefore, there are 19 digits in the number $2^{61} - 1$.

One atom of carbon is found to have a mass of $1 \cdot 994 \times 10^{-23}$ grams.

(i) Find the mass of 1,250,000 atoms of carbon.

(ii) A sample of carbon is made up of purely carbon atoms. Find the number of carbon atoms, in the form $a \times 10^n$, where $1 \le a < 10$ and $n \in \mathbb{N}$, within a carbon sample that has a mass of 8 kg.

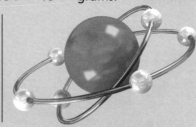

Solution

(i)
$$1 \text{ carbon atom} = 1 \cdot 994 \times 10^{-23}$$

$$1,250,000 \text{ carbon atoms} = (1,250,000)(1 \cdot 994 \times 10^{-23})$$

$$= 2 \cdot 4925 \times 10^{-17} \text{ grams}$$

(ii) 8 kg = 8,000 g

$$\text{Number of atoms} = \frac{\text{Total mass}}{\text{Mass of one atom}}$$

$$= \frac{8,000}{1 \cdot 994 \times 10^{-23}}$$

$$= 4 \cdot 012 \times 10^{26}$$

key point

1 kg = 1,000 g

Therefore, the sample contains 4×10^{26} carbon atoms.

6 Functions

aims

☐ To learn what a function is and how to recognise one
☐ To become familiar with the notation associated with functions
☐ To be able to solve problems involving functions
☐ To be able to form composite functions

A function is a rule that changes one number (input) into another number (output). Functions are often represented by the letters f, g, h or k. We can think of a function, f, as a number machine which changes an input, x, into an output, $f(x)$.

$f(x)$, which denotes the output, is read as 'f of x'.

Input

Output

key point

A function is also called a **mapping** or simply a **map**.

For example, let's represent the function 'double input and then add 5' by the letter f. This can be written as:

$$f: x \rightarrow 2x + 5 \quad \text{or} \quad f(x) = 2x + 5 \quad \text{or} \quad y = 2x + 5$$
$$(\text{input, output}) \quad = \quad (x, f(x)) = (x, 2x + 5) = (x, y)$$

One number is mapped onto another number.
In the above example, x is mapped onto $2x + 5$, usually written $f: x \rightarrow 2x + 5$.
A function connects **every** input in the domain to an output in the range.
A function is another way of writing an algebraic formula that links input to output.

key point

Note the different notations for function: $f: x \rightarrow$, $f(x)$, y.

Types of functions	
Linear	$f\!: x \rightarrow ax$ or $f\!: x \rightarrow ax + b$
Quadratic	$f\!: x \rightarrow ax^2 + bx + c$
Cubic	$f\!: x \rightarrow ax^3 + bx^2 + cx\,d$
Exponential	$f\!: x \rightarrow ab^x$

Input number

If $f\!:x \rightarrow 2x + 5$, then $f(3)$ means 'input 3 into the function', i.e. it is the result of applying the function f to the number 3.

$$f(3) = 2(3) + 5 = 6 + 5 = 11 \qquad (\text{input} = 3, \text{output} = 11)$$

$$(\text{input, output}) = (3, f(3)) = (3, 11)$$

A function does exactly the same to each input number and produces only one output number for each input number.

The set of input numbers is called the **domain**. The set of output numbers is called the **range**.

The set of **all possible outputs** is called the **codomain**.
In general, the range is a subset of the codomain. However, sometimes the range and the codomain are the same.

Consider the function f shown:
$f = \{(1, a), (2, b)(3, d), (4, d)\}$
from set X to set Y.

Domain: The set of elements from which the arrows leave: $\{1, 2, 3, 4\}$.
Range: The set of elements where the arrows arrive: $\{a, b, d\}$.
Codomain: The **possible** set of elements into which the arrows go: $\{a, b, c, d, e\}$.

Consider the function:

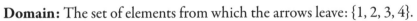

$$g : \mathbb{Z} \rightarrow \mathbb{Z} : x \rightarrow 2x + 1$$

Name Domain Codomain Rule (output)

key point

A domain or range described as:
$$[p, q) \text{ means } \{p \le x < q\}.$$
That is, the square bracket means p is included. The rounded bracket means q is not included.

It is vital that you are familiar with the basic **number systems:**

$\mathbb{N} = \{1, 2, 3, \ldots\}$, the set of natural numbers.

$\mathbb{Z} = \{\ldots -2, -1, 0, 1, 2, \ldots\}$, the set of integers.

$\mathbb{Q} = \{\text{fractions, } \dfrac{p}{q}, p, q \in \mathbb{Z}, q \neq 0, \text{ the set of rational numbers.}\}$

$\mathbb{R}/\mathbb{Q}$ = the set of irrational numbers (e.g. $\sqrt{3}$, π, etc.).

(See booklet of formulae and tables, page 23)

Example

State whether each of the following mapping diagrams is a function.
Give a reason for your answer in each case.

(i) 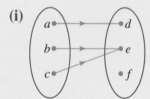 (ii)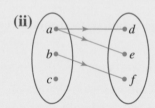

(iii) 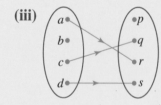 (iv)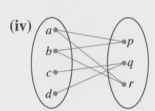

Solution

(i) Is a function, as each input has only one unique output.

(ii) Is not a function, as input a has two outputs.

(iii) Is not a function, as one element in the domain, b, has no output.

(iv) Is not a function, as inputs a and b have more than one output.

Example

A function f is defined as $f : x \rightarrow 3 - 2x$.

Find: (i) $f(0)$ (ii) $f(1)$ (iii) $f(2)$ (iv) $f(-1) - f(0)$ (v) Verify that $f(-3) > 0$.

Solution

(i) $f(x) = 3 - 2x$

$f(0) = 3 - 2(0)$

$f(0) = 3 - 0$

$f(0) = 3$

(ii) $f(x) = 3 - 2x$

$f(1) = 3 - 2(1)$

$f(1) = 3 - 2$

$f(1) = 1$

(iii) $f(x) = 3 - 2x$

$f(2) = 3 - 2(2)$

$f(2) = 3 - 4$

$f(2) = -1$

(iv) Find $f(-1) - f(0)$:

$f(x) = 3 - 2x$

$f(-1) = 3 - 2(-1)$

$f(-1) = 3 + 2$

$f(-1) = 5$ and $f(0) = 3$ (from (i))

$\therefore f(-1) - f(0) = 5 - 3 = 2$

(v) Find $f(-3)$ and see if it is greater than zero:

$f(-3) = 3 - 2(-3)$

$f(-3) = 3 + 6$

$f(-3) = 9$, which is greater than zero

$\therefore f(-3) > 0$

Example

A function f is defined as $f : x \rightarrow x^2 - 3x - 4$.

Find: (i) $f(1)$ (ii) $f(3)$ (iii) $3[f(-2)]$ (v) Find two values of x for which $f(x) = 0$.

Solution

(i) $f(x) = x^2 - 3x - 4$

$f(1) = (1)^2 - 3(1) - 4$

$f(1) = 1 - 3 - 4$

$f(1) = -6$

(ii) $f(x) = x^2 - 3x - 4$

$f(3) = (3)^2 - 3(3) - 4$

$f(3) = 9 - 9 - 4$

$f(3) = -4$

(iii) To find $3[f(-2)]$ we must first find the value of $f(-2)$:

$$f(x) = x^2 - 3x - 4$$
$$f(-2) = (-2)^2 - 3(-2) - 4$$
$$f(-2) = 4 + 6 - 4$$
$$f(-2) = 6$$
$$\therefore 3[f(-2)] = 3(6)$$
$$3[f(-2)] = 18$$

(iv) To find the values for x for which $f(x) = 0$, let $f(x) = 0$ and solve the quadratic.

$$f(x) = x^2 - 3x - 4$$

$$0 = x^2 - 3x - 4 \qquad \text{(let } f(x) = 0)$$
$$0 = (x - 4)(x + 1) \qquad \text{(factorise)}$$
$$x - 4 = 0 \quad \text{or} \quad x + 1 = 0$$
$$x = 4 \quad \text{or} \quad x = -1$$

$f : x \rightarrow x^2 + 1$ and $g : x \rightarrow 2x$ are two functions defined on $\mathbb{R}$.

(i) Find $f(\sqrt{3})$ and $g(1)$.

(ii) Find the value of λ for which $f(\sqrt{3}) = \lambda g(1)$, where $\lambda \in \mathbb{R}$.

(iii) Find the values of x for which $f(x) = g(x)$.

Solution

(i) $f(x) = x^2 + 1$ $g(x) = 2x$
       $f(\sqrt{3}) = (\sqrt{3})^2 + 1$ $g(1) = 2(1)$
       $f(\sqrt{3}) = 3 + 1$ $g(1) = 2$
       $f(\sqrt{3}) = 4$

(ii) $f(\sqrt{3}) = \lambda g(1)$

$$4 = \lambda(2)$$
$$2 = \lambda$$

(iii)

$$f(x) = g(x)$$
$$x^2 + 1 = 2x$$
$$x^2 - 2x + 1 = 0$$
$$(x - 1)(x - 1) = 0$$
$$x - 1 = 0 \quad \text{or} \quad x - 1 = 0$$
$$x = 1 \quad \text{or} \quad x = 1$$

Example

A function f is defined as $f: x \rightarrow 3x - 2$.

Find the missing numbers, p, q and r.

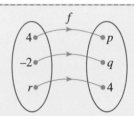

Solution

$f: x \rightarrow 3x - 2$	$f: x \rightarrow 3x - 2$	To find r, we are given an equation
$f(4) = 3(4) - 2$	$f(-2) = 3(-2) - 2$	in disguise. Output $= 4$, find input r:
$= 12 - 2$	$= -6 - 2$	$f(r) = 4$
$= 10$	$= -8$	$3r - 2 = 4$
$\therefore p = 10$	$\therefore q = -8$	$3r = 6$
		$r = 2$

The picture shows a wheel with six equally-spaced spokes. The spokes are labelled A, B, C, D, E and F.

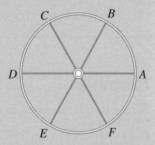

(i) The wheel is rotated anticlockwise so that the point A is mapped onto point C. What is the angle of rotation?

(ii) Complete the following ordered pairs, where the input value is the original position and the output value is the mapped position.

$\{(A, C), (B, \ ), (\ , E), (\ , \ ), (\ , \ ), (\ , \ )\}$

Solution

(i) Since there are six spokes, the wheel is divided into six sectors.

$$\text{Angle in each sector} = \frac{360°}{6} = 60°$$

Rotating the wheel anticlockwise so that point A moves to point C means it has been rotated by two sectors. Therefore, the angle of rotation $= 2(60°) = 120°$.

(ii) A moves to C, B moves to D, C moves to E,

D moves to F, E moves to A and F moves to B.

So the ordered pairs are: $\{(A, C), (B, D), (C, E), (D, F), (E, A), (F, B)\}$.

Example

A function f is defined as $f: x \rightarrow 2x - 5$. Complete the following four couples:

(i) $(3, \ )$ (ii) $(-3, \ )$ (iii) $(\ , 3)$ (iv) $(\ , -7)$

Solution

(i) $f: x \rightarrow 2x - 5$ $(3, \ )$

When $x = 3$, find y:

$f(3) = 2(3) - 5$

$\quad = 6 - 5$

$\quad = 1$

Therefore, the couple is $(3, 1)$.

(ii) $f: x \rightarrow 2x - 5$ $(-3, \ )$

When $x = -3$, find y:

$f(-3) = 2(-3) - 5$

$\quad = -6 - 5$

$\quad = -11$

Therefore, the couple is $(-3, -11)$.

(iii) $f: x \rightarrow 2x - 5$ $(\ , 3)$

When $y = 3$, find x:

$3 = 2x - 5$

$3 + 5 = 2x$

$8 = 2x$

$4 = x$

Therefore, the couple is $(4, 3)$.

(iv) $f: x \rightarrow 2x - 5$ $(\ , -7)$

When $y = -7$, find x:

$-7 = 2x - 5$

$-7 + 5 = 2x$

$-2 = 2x$

$-1 = x$

Therefore, the couple is $(-1, -7)$.

Example

A function f is defined as $f: x \rightarrow 3(2)^x$ where $x \in \mathbb{R}$.

Find: (i) $f(1)$ (ii) $f(0)$ (iii) $f(-2)$

(iv) Find the value of x for which $f(x) = 96$.

Solution

(i) $f(x) = 3(2)^x$

$f(1) = 3(2)^1$

$f(1) = 3(2) \quad (2^1 = 2)$

$f(1) = 6$

(ii) $f(x) = 3(2)^x$

$f(0) = 3(2)^0$

$f(0) = 3(1) \quad (2^0 = 1)$

$f(0) = 3$

(iii) $f(x) = 3(2)^x$

$f(-2) = 3(2)^{-2}$

$f(-2) = 3\left(\dfrac{1}{4}\right)$

$f(-2) = \dfrac{3}{4}$

(iv) $f(x) = 3(2)^x$

$96 = 3(2)^x$

$32 = (2)^x$ (divide both sides by 3)

$2^5 = 2^x$ (from indices $32 = 2^5$)

$5 = x$

$g : x \rightarrow ax^2 + bx + 1$ is a function defined on $\mathbb{R}$.

(i) If $g(1) = 0$ and $g(2) = 3$, write down two equations in a and b.

(ii) Hence, calculate the value of a and the value of b.

Solution

(i) We are told $g(1) = 0$:

$g(x) = ax^2 + bx + 1$

$g(1) = a(1)^2 + b(1) + 1$

$0 = a(1) + b + 1$ $(g(1) = 0)$

$-1 = a + b$ (equation ①)

We are told $g(2) = 3$:

$g(x) = ax^2 + bx + 1$

$g(2) = a(2)^2 + b(2) + 1$

$3 = a(4) + 2b + 1$ $(g(2) = 3)$

$3 = 4a + 2b + 1$

$2 = 4a + 2b$

$1 = 2a + b$ (equation ②)

(ii) Solving the equations simultaneously:

① $-1 = a + b$ $(\times -1)$

② $\underline{1 = 2a + b}$

$1 = -a - b$

$\underline{1 = 2a + b}$ (add)

$2 = a$

$-1 = a + b$

$-1 = 2 + b$ (let $a = 2$)

$-3 = b$

Composite functions

When one function is followed by another function, the result is a **composite** function.

Applying function g after applying function f is written in three different ways:

| 1. $g \circ f(x)$ | 2. $g\,f(x)$ | 3. $g[f(x)]$ |

All are pronounced 'g after f' and means 'do f followed by g'.

Consider the two functions $f(x) = x + 3$ and $g(x) = 5 - 2x$, where the domain of f is $\{1, 2, 3, 4\}$ and the domain of g is the range of f.

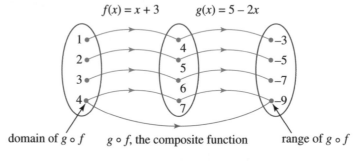

domain of $g \circ f$ $g \circ f$, the composite function   range of $g \circ f$

$$g \circ f = \{(1, -3), (2, -5), (3, -7), (4, -9)\}$$

We can work out a single **rule** for the composite function.

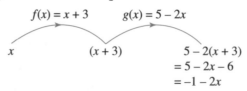

$$x \qquad (x + 3) \qquad \begin{aligned} 5 &- 2(x + 3) \\ &= 5 - 2x - 6 \\ &= -1 - 2x \end{aligned}$$

In this case, $g\,f(x) = -1 - 2x$.

Check: $g\,f(3) = -1 - 2(3) = -1 - 6 = -7$ (same as before)

Example

Given $f(x) = 6x + 5$ and $g(x) = 1 - 3x$, find:

(i) $g(2)$ (ii) $fg(2)$ (iii) $g \circ f(1)$ (iv) $gf(x)$

Solution

(i) $g(x) = 1 - 3x$

$g(2) = 1 - 3(2)$

$g(2) = 1 - 6$

$g(2) = -5$

(ii) $fg(2)$

From (i) $g(2) = -5$

$\therefore fg(2) = f(-5)$

$f(-5)$ (since $g(2) = -5$)

$f(-5) = 6(-5) + 5$

$f(-5) = -30 + 5$

$f(-5) = -25$

(iii) $g \circ f(1)$

Find $f(1) : f(1) = 6(1) + 5 = 11$

$g \circ f(1) = g(11)$

$g(11) = 1 - 3(11)$

$g(11) = 1 - 33 = -32$

(iv) $gf(x)$

$g(6x + 5) = 1 - 3(6x + 5)$

$g(6x + 5) = 1 - 18x - 15$

$g(6x + 5) = -14 - 18x$

$\therefore gf(x) = -14 - 18x$

exam
Q

$f(x) = x^2 + 3$ and $g(x) = 2x - 1$, where $x \in \mathbb{R}$.

(i) Evaluate $f g(3)$.

(ii) Evaluate $g[f(-2)]$.

(iii) Find the values for x for which $f \circ g(x) = 12$.

(iv) Find $f^2(x)$ in terms of x.

Solution

(i) $f g(3) = f(2(3) - 1)$

$= f(6 - 1)$

$= f(5)$

$= (5)^2 + 3$

$= 25 + 3$

$= 28$

(ii) $g[f(-2)] = g[(-2)^2 + 3]$

$= g[4 + 3]$

$= g[7]$

$= 2(7) - 1$

$= 14 - 1$

$= 13$

(iii) $f \circ g(x) = 12$

$f(g(x)) = 12$

$f(2x - 1) = 12$

$(2x - 1)^2 + 3 = 12$

$4x^2 - 4x + 1 + 3 = 12$

$4x^2 - 4x + 4 - 12 = 0$

$4x^2 - 4x - 8 = 0$

$x^2 - x - 2 = 0$

$(x + 1)(x - 2) = 0$

$x = -1 \quad \text{or} \quad x = 2$

(iv) $f^2(x) = f[f(x)]$

$= f(x^2 + 3)$

$= (x^2 + 3)^2 + 3$

$= x^4 + 6x^2 + 9 + 3$

$= x^4 + 6x^2 + 12$

key
point

$f^2(x)$ does not mean
'f squared' $f^2(x) = f[f(x)]$
This means to apply f twice

The number of people who visit an art exhibition can be modelled by $A(d) = 3,500d - 400d^2 - 1,000$, where $A(d)$ represents the attendance at the exhibition d days after it opens. The profit made by the gallery can be modelled by

$P(n) = 2n - 2,500$, where $P(n)$ represents the profit in euro for the gallery on a day when n people attend.

(i) Find the number of people who were in attendance on the fourth day of the exhibition.

(ii) Find the profit made on the fourth day of the exhibition.

(iii) Use these functions to find a new function that will give the profit made by the gallery d days after the exhibition opens.

(iv) How much profit does the gallery make on the third day of the exhibition?

Solution

(i) The number of people who visited is modelled by the function $A(d)$, so we need to find the value of $A(d)$ when $d = 4$:

$$A(4) = 3,500(4) - 400(4)^2 - 1,000$$
$$= 14,000 - 6,400 - 1,000$$
$$= 6,600$$

Therefore, 6,600 people attended the exhibition on the fourth day.

(ii) Find the value of $P(n)$ when $n = 6,600$:

$$P(6,600) = 2(6,600) - 2,500$$
$$= 13,200 - 2,500$$
$$= 10,700$$

Therefore, the profit on day 4 was €10,700.

(iii) To find the profit in terms of d, we need to find the function P in terms of d. That is, to find $P \circ A(d)$:

$$P(A(d)) = 2(A(d)) - 2,500 \quad \text{(substitute } A(d) \text{ into the } P(a) \text{ function)}$$
$$= 2(3,500d - 400d^2 - 1,000) - 2,500$$
$$= 7,000d - 800d^2 - 2,000 - 2,500$$
$$= 7,000d - 800d^2 - 4,500$$

(iv) To find the profit on the third day, find the value of P when $d = 3$. We can use the composite function $P(A(d))$ and find $P(A(3))$:

$$P(A(3)) = 7,000(3) - 800(3)^2 - 4,500$$
$$= 21,000 - 7,200 - 4,500$$
$$= 9,300$$

Therefore, the profit on day 3 was €9,300.

7 Graphing Functions

You must be able to graph a given function and recognise the graphs of certain functions.

To recognise if a graph represents a function, use the vertical line test:

Vertical line test

If any vertical line (red line in picture) cuts the graph at only one point, then the graph represents a function.

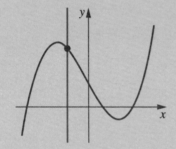

If any vertical line (red line in picture) cuts the graph at more than one point, then the graph does **not** represent a function.

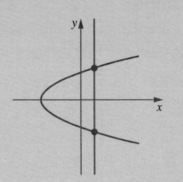

Example

Use the vertical line test to determine if each of the following is the graph of a function where $x \in \mathbb{R}$.

(i)

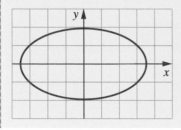

(ii)

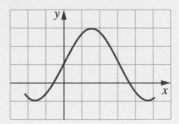

(iii)

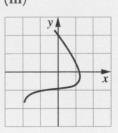

Solution

(i) A vertical line would cross the graph twice in some places, therefore it is not a function.

(ii) Every vertical line would only cross the graph once, therefore it is a function.

(iii) A vertical line would cross the graph more than once in some places. Therefore, it is not a function.

Continuous functions

A function is continuous when its graph is a single unbroken curve. To recognise a function which is not continuous (discontinuous), look out for holes, jumps or vertical asymptotes (where the function heads up or down towards infinity).

key point

The graph of a continuous function can be drawn without lifting your pen off the page.

Example

State whether the following functions are continuous or discontinuous. Give a reason for your answer.

Solution

(i)

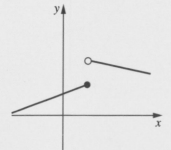

(ii)

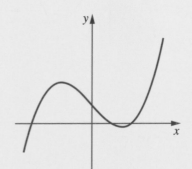

(iii)

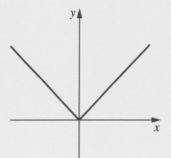

(iv)

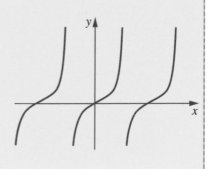

Solution

(i) Discontinuous, because the graph jumps.

(ii) Continuous, because the graph is a single unbroken curve.

(iii) Continuous, because the graph is a single unbroken curve.

(iv) Discontinuous, because the graph jumps.

Limit of a function

The limit of a function at a point is the value a function reaches as you approach that point from both sides.

Example

(i) $f : x \rightarrow 3x - 2$ is a function where $x \in \mathbb{R}$. Complete the following tables.

x	3x − 2	f(x)
1·5		
1·6		
1·7		
1·8		
1·9		
1·95		

x	3x − 2	f(x)
2·5		
2·4		
2·3		
2·2		
2·1		
2·05		

(ii) Hence or otherwise, find the limit of the function as x approaches 2.

Solution

(i) Completed tables:

x	3x − 2	f(x)
1·5	3(1·5) − 2	2·5
1·6	3(1·6) − 2	2·8
1·7	3(1·7) − 2	3·1
1·8	3(1·8) − 2	3·4
1·9	3(1·9) − 2	3·7
1·95	3(1·95) − 2	3·85

x	3x − 2	f(x)
2·5	3(2·5) − 2	5·5
2·4	3(2·4) − 2	5·2
2·3	3(2·3) − 2	4·9
2·2	3(2·2) − 2	4·6
2·1	3(2·1) − 2	4·3
2·05	3(2·05) − 2	4·15

(ii) From the tables, we can see that as the value for x gets closer to 2 from both directions, the value for $f(x)$ gets closer to 4.

Therefore, we can conclude that the limit of the function as x approaches 2 is 4.

Alternative method:

Find the value of $f(x)$ when $x = 2$:
$$f(2) = 3(2) - 2$$
$$f(2) = 6 - 2$$
$$f(2) = 4$$

Therefore, the limit of $f(x)$ as x approaches 2 is 4.

If a function $f(x)$ is continuous at a particular input value, $x = k$, it has a limit at that value. This may be written as $\lim_{x \to k} f(x) = f(k)$. The converse is also true, i.e. if a function has a limit at a value, it is continuous at that value.

Graphing functions

To graph a function, find points which satisfy the function by substituting values in for x and finding the corresponding y-values. Plot these points and join them up to obtain the graph of the function.

To better understand the graphs of functions, you should practise graphing functions on a graphing calculator or graphing software, such a Geogebra (free to download from www.geogebra.org).

Linear functions

A linear function is usually given by $f : x \to ax + b$, where $a, b \in \mathbb{Q}, x \in \mathbb{R}$.

To graph a linear function you need two points.

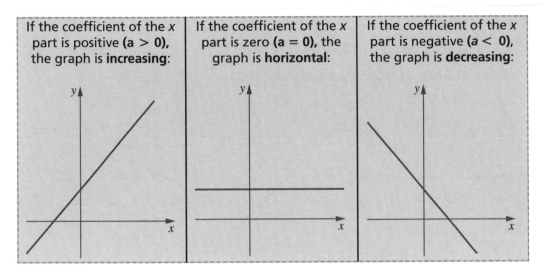

If the coefficient of the x part is positive **(a > 0)**, the graph is **increasing**:	If the coefficient of the x part is zero **(a = 0)**, the graph is **horizontal**:	If the coefficient of the x part is negative **(a < 0)**, the graph is **decreasing**:

key point

Graphing linear functions is also covered under the topic of coordinate geometry of the line, which can be found in Less Stress More Success, Leaving Certificate Ordinary Level Paper 2.

Example

(i) Using the same axes and scale, graph the functions: $y = 3 - x$ and $2y = x + 3$ in the domain $-5 \leq x \leq 5$.

(ii) Use your graph to estimate the point of intersection between these two functions.

Solution

(i) In order to graph a linear function, find the two points at the end of each line segment. However, any two points in the domain will work.

Line 1: $y = 3 - x$		**Line 2: $2y = x + 3$**	
If $x = -5$	If $x = 5$	If $x = -5$	If $x = 5$
$y = 3 - (-5)$	$y = 3 - 5$	$2y = -5 + 3$	$2y = 5 + 3$
$y = 8$	$y = -2$	$2y = -2$	$2y = 8$
$(-5, 8)$	$(5, -2)$	$y = -1$	$y = 4$
		$(-5, -1)$	$(5, 4)$

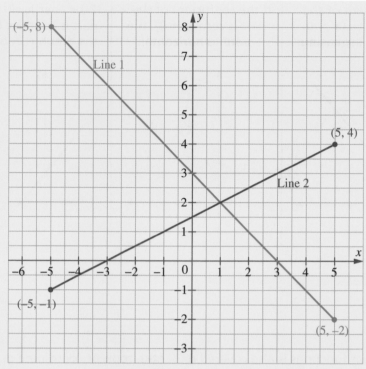

(ii) From the graph, we can estimate the point of intersection of the functions to be $(1, 2)$.

exam Q

John is given two sunflower plants. One plant is 16 cm high and the other is 24 cm high. John measures the height of each plant at the same time every day for a week. He notes that the 16 cm plant grows 4 cm each day, and the 24 cm plant grows 3·5 cm each day.

(i) Draw a table showing the heights of the two plants each day for the week. Start on the day that John got them.

(ii) Write down two formulas – one for each plant – to represent the plants' height on any given day. State clearly the meaning of any letters used in your formulas.

(iii) John assumes that the plants will continue to grow at the same rates. Draw graphs to represent the heights of the two plants over the first four weeks.

(iv) From your diagram, write down the point of intersection of the two graphs. Explain what the point of intersection means with respect to the two plants. Your answer should refer to the meaning of *both* coordinates.

(v) Check your answer to part (iv) using your formulae from part (ii).

(vi) The point of intersection can be found either by reading the graph of John's model by using algebra. State one advantage of finding it using algebra.

(vii) John's model for the growth of the plants might not be correct. State one limitation of the model that might affect the point of intersection and its interpretation.

Solution

(i) Start at day zero. On day one, the heights of the plants have increased by 4 cm and 3·5 cm respectively:

Plant A	
Day	Height
0	16
1	20
2	24
3	28
4	32
5	36
6	40

Plant B	
Day	Height
0	24
1	27·5
2	31
3	34·5
4	38
5	41·5
6	45

(ii) Plant A: Height = 16 + 4(no. of days) Plant B: Height = 24 + 3·5 no. of days)

Plant A: $h = 16 + 4d$ Plant B: $h = 24 + 3·5d$

key point

A linear function can be represented by:

y = starting value + (rate of growth)x

This is the same as the equation for a line

$$y = mx + c$$

where: m = rate of growth = slope

c = starting value = y-intercept

(see booklet of formulae and tables, page 18)

(iii) Graphing the growth of both plants over 28 days:

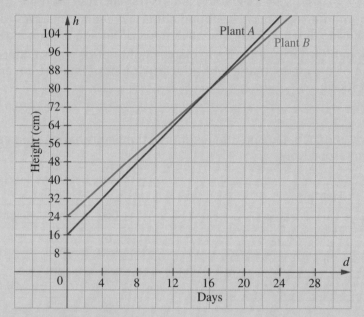

(iv) From the graphs, we can estimate the point of intersection to be (15·5, 78). This means that on day 16, both plants are at a height of 80 cm.

(v) Solving the equations: $h = 16 + 4d$ and $h = 24 + 3·5d$

By comparison, let $h = h$:

$16 + 4d = 24 + 3·5d$	Let $d = 16$:
$4d - 3·5d = 24 - 16$	$h = 16 + 4d$
$0·5d = 8$ $(×2)$	$h = 16 + 4(16)$
$d = 16$	$h = 80$

Therefore, the point of intersection is (16, 80).

(vi) Using algebra will give the exact value of the point of intersection, which is more accurate than an estimate from the graph.

(vii) John's model assumes that the sunflowers continue to grow at a constant rate over a number of weeks. In reality, you would expect the rate of growth to slow down. Other factors, such as amount of light and water, could affect the growth rate also.

Quadratic functions

A quadratic function is usually given by $f : x \rightarrow ax^2 + bx + c$, where $a, b, c \in \mathbb{Q}, x \in \mathbb{R}$ and $a \neq 0$. Because of its shape, quite a few points are needed to accurately graph a quadratic function.

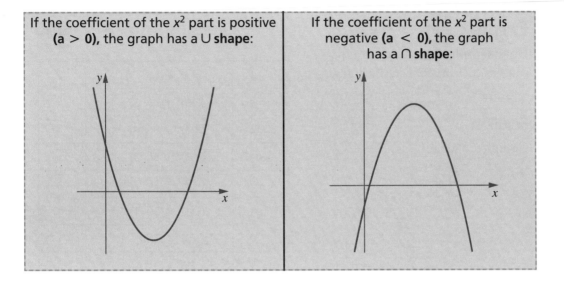

If the coefficient of the x^2 part is positive **(a > 0)**, the graph has a ∪ **shape**:

If the coefficient of the x^2 part is negative **(a < 0)**, the graph has a ∩ **shape**:

Nature of roots of a quadratic equation:

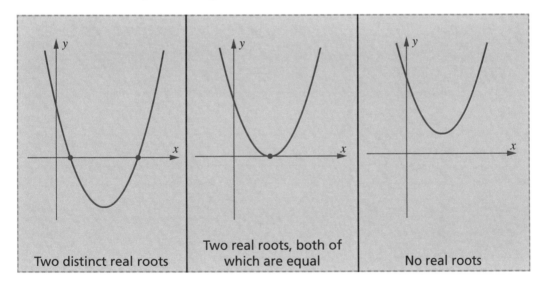

Two distinct real roots

Two real roots, both of which are equal

No real roots

Example

Draw a graph of the function
$f : x \rightarrow x^2 + 3x - 1$ in the domain
$-5 \leq x \leq 2$.

Solution

Complete a table:

x	$x^2 + 3x - 1$	y
−5	$(-5)^2 + 3(-5) - 1$	9
−4	$(-4)^2 + 3(-4) - 1$	3
−3	$(-3)^2 + 3(-3) - 1$	−1
−2	$(-2)^2 + 3(-2) - 1$	−3
−1	$(-1)^2 + 3(-1) - 1$	−3
0	$(0)^2 + 3(0) - 1$	−1
1	$(1)^2 + 3(1) - 1$	3
2	$(2)^2 + 3(2) - 1$	9

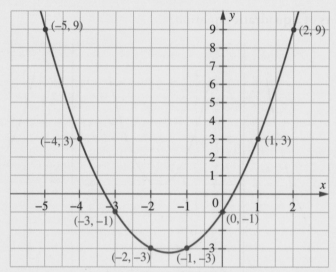

The ordered pairs are:
$(-5, 9), (-4, 3), (-3, -1), (-2, -3), (-1, -3), (0, -1), (1, 3)$ and $(2, 9)$.
Plot these points and join them up to graph the function $f(x)$.

Alternative method to finding the points:

$f(-5) = (-5)^2 + 3(-5) - 1 = 9$ $f(-1) = (-1)^2 + 3(-1) - 1 = -3$

$f(-4) = (-4)^2 + 3(-4) - 1 = 3$ $f(0) = (0)^2 + 3(0) - 1 = -1$

$f(-3) = (-3)^2 + 3(-3) - 1 = -1$ $f(1) = (1)^2 + 3(1) - 1 = 3$

$f(-2) = (-2)^2 + 3(-2) - 1 = -3$ $f(2) = (2)^2 + 3(2) - 1 = 9$

The ordered pairs are: $(-5, 9), (-4, 3), (-3, -1), (-2, -3), (-1, -3), (0, -1),$
$(1, 3)$ and $(2, 9)$.

Example

Shown is the graph of the function
$f : x \rightarrow 3 + 2x - x^2$ in the domain
$-2 \leq x \leq 4$.
Use the graph to find:

(i) The values of x for which $f(x) = 0$
(ii) The values of x for which $f(x) = 3$
(iii) The values of x for which $f(x) = -5$
(iv) The value of $f(1)$
(v) The value of $f(3\cdot5)$
(vi) The coordinates of the maximum point

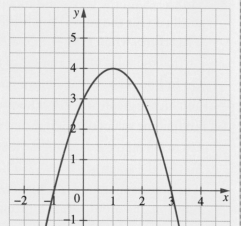

Solution

(i) To find the values of x for which
$f(x) = 0$ means to find the values of x
when $y = 0$.
Go to 0 on the y-axis and move across
horizontally in both directions until
you hit the graph. You hit the graph
at $x = -1$ and $x = 3$. **Therefore,**
when $f(x) = 0, x = -1$ and 3.

(ii) To find the values of x for which
$f(x) = 3$ means to find the values of
x when $y = 3$.
Go to 3 on the y-axis and move across
horizontally in both directions until
you hit the graph. You hit the graph
at $x = 0$ and $x = 2$. **Therefore, when**
$f(x) = 3, x = 0$ and 2 (red line).

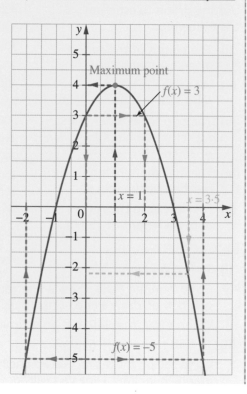

(iii) To find the values of x for which $f(x) = -5$ means to find the values of x when $y = -5$.

Go to -5 on the y-axis and move across horizontally in both directions until you hit the graph. You hit the graph at $x = -2$ and $x = 4$.
Therefore, when $f(x) = -5$, $x = -2$ and 4 (green line).

(iv) To find the value of $f(1)$ means to find the value of y when $x = 1$.

Go to 1 on the x-axis and move vertically until you hit the graph.

You hit the graph at $y = 4$. **Therefore, $f(1) = 4$ (blue line).**

(v) To find the values of $f(3\cdot5)$ means to find the values of y when $x = 3\cdot5$.

Go to $3\cdot5$ on the x-axis and move vertically until you hit the graph.

You hit the graph at $y = -2\cdot3$. **Therefore, $f(3\cdot5) = -2\cdot3$ (orange line).**

(vi) The maximum point it the highest point that the curve reaches. For this function, the coordinates of the **maximum point are (1, 4).**

A rocket is launched. Its height, h, in metres, t seconds after launch is modelled by
$h(t) = -16t^2 + 200t + 2$.

Use the graph to estimate the following.

(i) The height of the rocket after 2 seconds

(ii) When the rocket first reaches a height of 550 m

(iii) The two times when the rocket is at a height of 300 m

(iv) The maximum height reached by the rocket

(v) For how long the rocket is above a height of 150 m

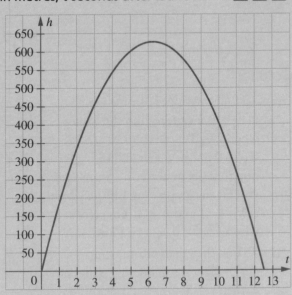

Solution

(i) To find h when $t = 2$:

Go to 2 on the t-axis, draw a line vertically upwards (green line) until you hit the graph, then draw a line horizontally across to read the value for h at this point.

When $t = 2$, $h = 340$ m is an estimate.

(ii) To find t when $h = 550$ m:

Go to 550 on the h-axis, draw a line horizontally across (blue line) until you hit the graph, then draw a line vertically downwards to read the value for t at this point.

When $h = 550$, $t = 4$ seconds for the first time.

(iii) To find two values for t
when $h = 300$ m:

Go to 300 on the h-axis,
draw a line horizontally
across (pink line) until you
hit the graph, then draw a
line vertically downwards to
read the value for t at these
points.

Estimate when $h = 300$,
$t = 1·7$ secs and 10·8 secs.

(iv) To find maximum height,
draw a line horizontally
across from the top of the
curve (orange line) to read
the value for h at this point.
Estimate $h = 630$ m at
maximum height.

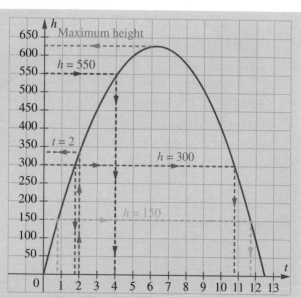

(v) To find two values for t when $h = 150$ m:

Go to 150 on the h-axis, draw a line horizontally across (yellow line) until you
hit the graph, then draw a line vertically downwards to read the value for t at
these points.

Estimate when $h = 150$, $t = 0·75$ secs and 11·75 secs.

Therefore, the rocket is above 150 m for between $11·75 - 0·75 = 11$ seconds.

The function $f(x) = x^2 + bx + c$ is graphed on
the right. The curve contains the point $(-3, -4)$
and it crosses the x-axis at the point $(1, 0)$.

(i) Write down two equations in b and c.

(ii) Solve these equations to find the values of
b and c.

(iii) Use these values for b and c to write down
the function $f(x)$.

(iv) Use this function to find the coordinates of
the points P and Q.

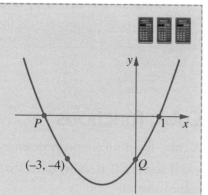

Solution

(i) Point $(1, 0)$ is on the function.
This means when $x = 1$, $y = 0$:

$y = x^2 + bx + c$

$0 = (1)^2 + b(1) + c$

$0 = 1 + b + c$

$-1 = b + c$ ①

Point $(-3, -4)$ is on the function.

This means when $x = -3$, $y = -4$:

$y = x^2 + bx + c$

$-4 = (-3)^2 + b(-3) + c$

$-4 = 9 - 3b + c$

$-13 = -3b + c$ ②

exam focus

> If a point is on the graph of a function, you can substitute its coordinates into the function.

(ii) Solving simultaneously:

① $b + c = -1$

② $\underline{-3b + c = -13}$ $(\times -1)$

     $b + c = -1$

     $\underline{3b - c = 13}$ (add)

       $4b = 12$

        $b = 3$

Let $b = 3$:

$b + c = -1$

$3 + c = -1$

$c = -1 - 3$

$c = -4$

(iii) $f(x) = x^2 + bx + c$ $b = 3$ and $c = -4$

$\therefore f(x) = x^2 + 3x - 4$

(iv) At x-axis, $y = 0$:

$y = x^2 + 3x - 4$

$0 = x^2 + 3x - 4$

$0 = (x + 4)(x - 1)$

$x + 4 = 0$ or $x - 1 = 0$

$x = -4$ or $x = 1$

Crosses x-axis at $(-4, 0)$ and $(1, 0)$.

Therefore, point $P = (-4, 0)$.

At y-axis, $x = 0$:

$y = x^2 + 3x - 4$

$y = (0)^2 + 3(0) - 4$

$y = -4$

Therefore, point $Q = (0, -4)$.

Cubic functions

A cubic function is usually given by $f : x \rightarrow ax^3 + bx^2 + cx + d$, where $a, b, c, d \in \mathbb{Z}$, $x \in \mathbb{R}$ and $a \neq 0$. Because of its shape, quite a few points are needed to accurately graph a cubic function.

If the coefficient of the x^3 part is positive $(a > 0)$, the graph **starts by increasing**:	If the coefficient of the x^3 part is negative $(a < 0)$, the graph **starts by decreasing**:
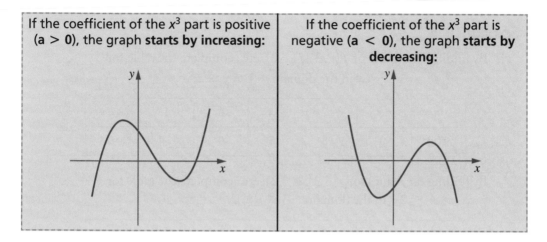	

Nature of roots of a cubic equation:

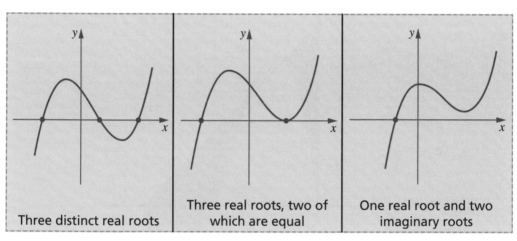

Three distinct real roots	Three real roots, two of which are equal	One real root and two imaginary roots

Example

(i) On the same axes and scales, graph the functions
$$f: x \rightarrow x^3 + x^2 - 6x \text{ and } g: x \rightarrow 4 - 2x \text{ in the domain } -3 \leq x \leq 2.$$
Use the graph to find:
(ii) The points of intersection between $f(x)$ and $g(x)$
(iii) The range of values of x for which $f(x) < g(x)$
(iv) The range of values of x for which $f(x) > g(x)$

Solution

(i) By finding the values of $f(-3), f(-2)$, etc., complete the table for
$f : x \rightarrow x^3 + x^2 - 6x$ in the domain $-3 \leq x \leq 2$:

x	-3	-2	-1	0	1	2
f(x)	0	8	6	0	-4	0

By finding the values for $g(-3), g(-2)$, etc., complete the table for
$g : x \rightarrow 4 - 2x$ in the domain $-3 \leq x \leq 2$:

x	-3	-2	-1	0	1	2
g(x)	10	8	6	4	2	0

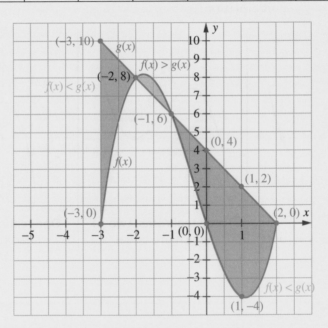

(ii) From the graph, we can see that $f(x)$ intersects $g(x)$ at the points
$(-2, 8), (-1, 6)$ and $(2, 0)$.

(iii) Find the range of values of x for which $f(x) < g(x)$ means to find the values of x
for which the $f(x)$ graph is below the $g(x)$ graph.
This occurs everywhere below $x = -2$ and between -1 and 2.

Therefore, $f(x) < g(x)$ for $-3 < x < -2$ and $-1 < x < 2$ (orange shaded area on graph).

(iv) Find the range of values of x for which $f(x) > g(x)$ means to find the values of x for which the $f(x)$ graph is above the $g(x)$ graph.

This occurs between -2 and -1. Therefore, $f(x) > g(x)$ for $-2 < x < -1$ (blue shaded area on graph).

f (x) will also be above g(x) after x = 2, but this is outside of our domain.

Let $g: x \rightarrow 2x^3 - 2x^2 - 7x + 3$ for $x \in \mathbb{R}$.

(i) Complete the table.

x	−2	−1·5	−1	−0·5	0	0·5	1	1·5	2	2·5
g(x)			6					−5·25		

(ii) Draw the graph of f(x) in the domain $-2 \leq x \leq 2.5$.

(iii) Estimate the coordinates of the local maximum and the local minimum points.

(iv) Use your graph to find the range of values of x for which g(x) is decreasing.

(v) Estimate the values of x for which g(x) = 0.

(vi) Use your graph to estimate the solutions to the equation $2x^3 - 2x^2 - 7x + 3 = -2$.

Solution

(i) By finding the values for g(−2), g(−1·5), etc., complete the table for $g: x \rightarrow 2x^3 - 2x^2 - 7x + 3$ in the domain $-2 \leq x \geq 2.5$:

x	−2	−1·5	−1	−0·5	0	0·5	1	1·5	2	2·5
g(x)	−7	2·25	6	5·75	3	−0·75	−4	−5·25	−3	4·25

(ii) The points are plotted and the graph is drawn. (see diagram).

(iii) Local maximum point is the point at the top of the curve, estimated as $(-0.8, 6.3)$.

Local minimum point is the point at the bottom of the curve, estimated as $(1.5, -5.3)$ (marked as the red dot on the graph).

(iv) $g(x)$ is decreasing (moving downwards) as it moves from the maximum point to the minimum point. Based on the values from (iii), $g(x)$ is decreasing for $-0.8 < x < 1.5$.

(v) Find x when $g(x) = 0$ means to find x when $y = 0$.

$y = 0$ along the x-axis.

The graph crosses the x-axis where $x = -1.7, 0.4$ and 2.3 (marked as green dots on the graph).

Therefore, $x = -1.7, 0.4$ and 2.3 for $g(x) = 0$.

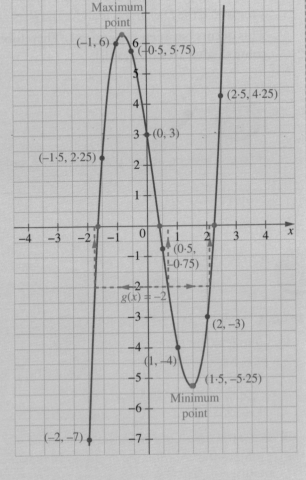

(vi) $2x^3 - 2x^2 - 7x + 3 = -2$

$g(x) = -2$ (since $g(x) = 2x^3 - 2x^2 - 7x + 3$)

To solve this equation, we need to find the values of x when $y = -2$ on the graph (red lines on the graph). When $y = -2$, $x = -1.8, 0.7, 2.1$.

Therefore, the solutions to the equation $2x^3 - 2x^2 - 7x + 3 = -2$ are $x = -1.8, 0.7, 2.1$.

(i) Graph the function $f : x \rightarrow x^3 - x^2 - 8x + 17$ in the domain $-3 \leq x \leq 3$.

(ii) Hence, use the trapezoidal rule to estimate the area between the curve and the x-axis.

Solution

(i) By finding the values for $f(-3)$, $f(-2)$, etc., complete the table for $f : x \rightarrow x^3 - x^2 - 8x + 17$ in the domain $-3 \leq x \leq 3$:

x	−3	−2	−1	0	1	2	3
f(x)	5	21	23	17	9	5	11

Graphing these points:

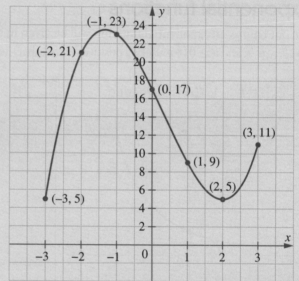

(ii) To use the trapezoidal rule, we must divide the area into vertical strips:

$w = 1$,

$h_1 = 5$, $h_2 = 21$, $h_3 = 23$,

$h_4 = 17$, $h_5 = 9$, $h_6 = 5$, $h_7 = 11$

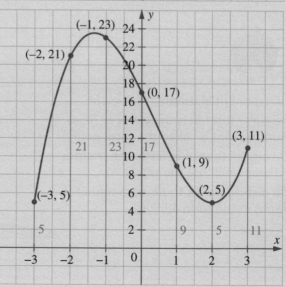

$$\text{Area} = \frac{w}{2}[h_1 + h_7 + 2(h_2 + h_3 + h_4 + h_5 + h_6)]$$ (see booklet of tables and formule and tables, page 12)

$$= \frac{1}{2}[5 + 11 + 2(21 + 23 + 17 + 9 + 5)]$$

$$= \frac{1}{2}[16 + 2(75)]$$

$$= \frac{1}{2}[16 + 150]$$

$$= \frac{1}{2}[166]$$

$$= 83 \text{ sq. units}$$

exam focus

Notice the link to the topic of area, which is normally associated with Paper 2. Covered in Less Stress More Success, Leaving Certificate, Paper 2.

Exponential functions

On our course, an exponential function will be given in the form $f: x \rightarrow ab^x$, where $a \in \mathbb{N}$ and b, $x \in \mathbb{R}$ and $b > 0$ (b must be a positive real number) and $a \neq 0$.

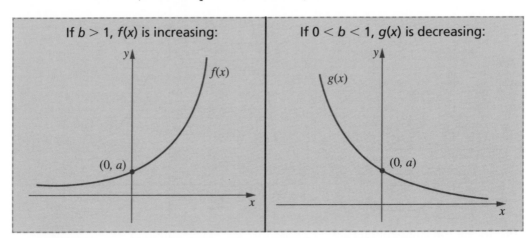

If $b > 1$, $f(x)$ is increasing:

$f(x)$

$(0, a)$

If $0 < b < 1$, $g(x)$ is decreasing:

$g(x)$

$(0, a)$

key point

For exponential graphs, $f(x) = ab^x$.

The curve intersects the y-axis at $(0, a)$ and this point is called the focal point.

The bigger the value for b, the sharper the graph will rise (or fall).

The picture shows three expanential graphs in the form $5(6^x)$.

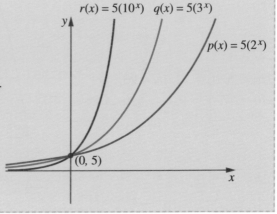

$r(x) = 5(10^x)$ $q(x) = 5(3^x)$

$p(x) = 5(2^x)$

$(0, 5)$

The number of bacteria, $B(t)$, in a sample after t hours can be represented by the model:

$$B(t) = 50(2^t).$$

(i) Graph the number of bacteria for the first 5 hours.

(ii) Use the graph to estimate the number of bacteria present after 4·5 hours.

(iii) Use the graph to estimate after how many hours there are 600 bacteria present in the sample.

Solution

(i)

t	$50(2^t)$	$B(t)$
0	$50(2^0)$	50
1	$50(2^1)$	100
2	$50(2^2)$	200
3	$50(2^3)$	400
4	$50(2^4)$	800
5	$50(2^5)$	1,600

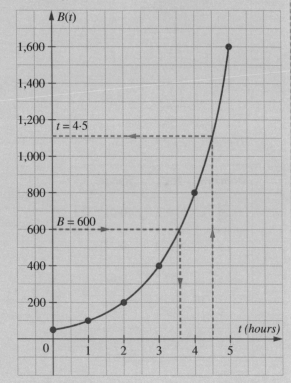

(ii) From the graph:

when $t = 4·5$ hours,

$B(4·5) = 1,140$ (red line)

(iii) From the graph:

when $B = 600$, $t = 3·6$ hours. (green line)

Example

(i) On the same axes and scales, graph the functions

$$f(x) \rightarrow \left(\frac{1}{2}\right)^x \text{ and } g(x) \rightarrow 2(3^x) \text{ in the domain } -3 \leq x \leq 1.$$

(ii) From your graph, estimate the point of intersection of f and g.

(iii) Find the range of value of x for which $g(x) < f(x)$.

Solution

(i) To graph $f(x) \rightarrow \left(\dfrac{1}{2}\right)^x$:

Domain	$\left(\dfrac{1}{2}\right)^x$	Range
-3	$\left(\dfrac{1}{2}\right)^{-3}$	8
-2	$\left(\dfrac{1}{2}\right)^{-2}$	4
-1	$\left(\dfrac{1}{2}\right)^{-1}$	2
0	$\left(\dfrac{1}{2}\right)^{0}$	1
1	$\left(\dfrac{1}{2}\right)^{1}$	0·5

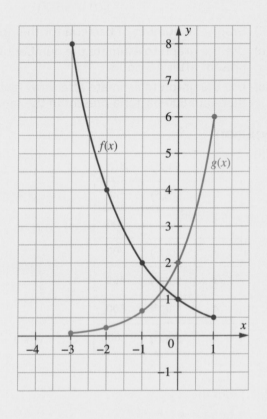

To graph $g(x) \rightarrow 2(3^x)$:

Domain	$2(3^x)$	Range
-3	$2(3^{-3})$	0·07
-2	$2(3^{-2})$	0·22
-1	$2(3^{-1})$	0·67
0	$2(3^{0})$	1
1	$2(3^{1})$	6

(ii) From the graph, the point of intersection of $f(x)$ and $g(x)$ is estimated to be $(-0·4, 1·3)$.

(iii) $g(x) < f(x)$ for all values of x less than $-0·4$. Therefore, $g(x) < f(x)$ for $-3 < x < -0·4$ within our domain.

Transforming graphs

By adding and subtracting constant values (numbers), the position of a graph can be transformed (moved) in either the vertical or horizontal direction, or both.

key point

Transforming graphs in the veritcal direction

Adding a constant to a fuction moves the graph of the function vertically **upwards** by that constant.

In the diagram, $f(x) + 2$ is two units above $f(x)$.

Substracting a constant from a function moves the graph of the function vertically **downwards** by that constant.

In the diagram, $f(x) - 1$ is one unit below $f(x)$.

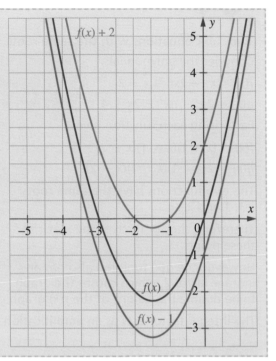

Example

(i) Graph the function $f : x \rightarrow 4^x$ in the domain $-1 \le x \le 2$.

(ii) On the same axis and scale, draw the graph of the function $h : x \rightarrow f(x) - 10$.

Solution

(i)

x	4^x	y
−1	4^{-1}	0·25
0	4^0	1
1	4^1	4
2	4^2	16

Ordered pairs:

$(-1, 0\cdot25), (0, 1), (1, 4)$ and $(2, 16)$.

Graph these points to get $f(x)$ (in blue).

(ii) $h : x \rightarrow f(x) - 10$ means that function $h(x)$ equals $f(x)$ minus 10.

The result of this is that the graph of $h(x)$ is the same shape as $f(x)$, but it is 10 units directly below the graph of $f(x)$.

Therefore, the points on $h(x)$ are $(-1, -9\cdot75), (0, -9), (1, -6)$ and $(2, 6)$.

Graph these points to get $h(x)$ (in red).

Two cubic equations with the same roots

Consider the polynomials:

$f(x) = x^3 - 2x^2 - x + 2$

$g(x) = 2x^3 - 4x^2 - 2x + 4$

Factorising each function gives:

$f(x) = (x + 1)(x - 1)(x - 2)$

$g(x) = 2(x + 1)(x - 1)(x - 2)$

The two functions have the same roots:
−1, 1 and 2.

Therefore, they both cross the x-axis at
these points.

However, the $g(x)$ function also has an
integer factor 2, which causes the graph
to be double the height of the $f(x)$ graph.

The integer factor acts as an **amplification** factor.

**Transforming graphs in the horizontal
direction**

Adding a constant to the x part of a
function moves the graph of the
function horizontally to the **left** by
that constant. In the diagram, $f(x + 2)$
is two units to the left of $f(x)$.

Subtracting a constant from the x part of
a function moves the graph of the
function horizontally to the **right** by that
constant. In the diagram, $f(x - 1)$ is one
unit to the right of $f(x)$.

In both cases, the result is the opposite to
what you would think.

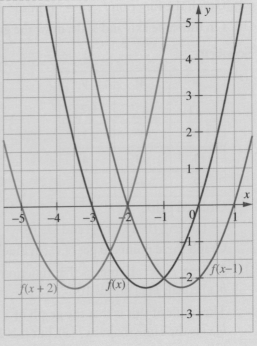

The function A (blue) is defined by the equation $y = x^2$.

By observation or otherwise, write down the equation of the functions B, C and D.

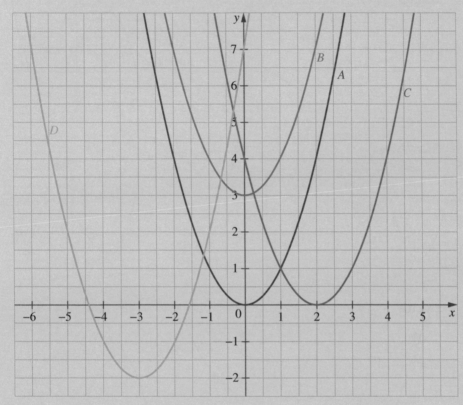

Solution

Graph B: 3 units vertically above graph A.

This means that we must add 3 to the equation for graph A.

Therefore, equation of B: $y = x^2 + 3$.

Graph C: 2 units to the right of graph A.

This means that the equation of C is the same as A, but with 2 subtracted from the x part.

Therefore, equation of C: $y = (x - 2)^2$.

Graph D: 3 units to the left of A **and** 2 units below A.

This means that we must add 3 to the x part **and** subtract 2 from the overall function.

Therefore, equation of D: $y = (x + 3)^2 - 2$.

exam
Q

Match the following 12 graphs to the given 12 functions.

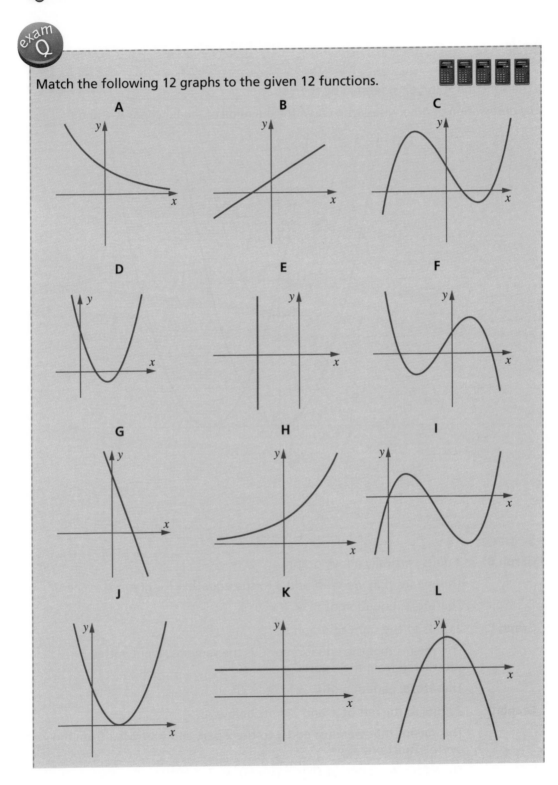

Functions

1. $y = x^2 - 8x + 16$

2. $y = 3$

3. $y = x^3 - 7x^2 + 10x$

4. $y = 3^x$

5. $x = -2$

6. $y = -x^3 - 2x^2 + 11x + 12$

7. $y = -x^2 + x - 6$

8. $y = -3x + 2$

9. $y = \left(\dfrac{1}{2}\right)^x$

10. $y = x^3 - 13x + 12$

11. $y = x^2 - 7x + 10$

12. $y = 2x + 5$

Solution

Graph	Function	Reason
A	$y = \left(\dfrac{1}{2}\right)^x$	Exponential graph moving downwards
B	$y = 2x + 5$	Linear function with a positive slope
C	$y = x^3 - 13x + 12$	Cubic graph which starts by moving upwards, so the x^3 term is positive
D	$y = x^2 - 7x + 10$	Quadratic function with two distinct roots
E	$x = -2$	Vertical line through the point $x = -2$
F	$y = -x^3 - 2x^2 + 11x + 12$	Cubic graph which starts by moving downwards, so the x^3 term is negative
G	$y = -3x + 2$	Linear function with a negative slope
H	$y = 3^x$	Exponential graph moving upward
I	$y = x^3 - 7x^2 + 10x$	Cubic graph where factorising shows that one root is zero
J	$y = x^2 - 8x + 16$	Quadratic graph with equal roots
K	$y = 3$	Horizontal line through the point $y = 3$
L	$y = -x^2 + x - 6$	Quadratic graph with a negative x^2 part means that it is a $\cap$-shaped graph

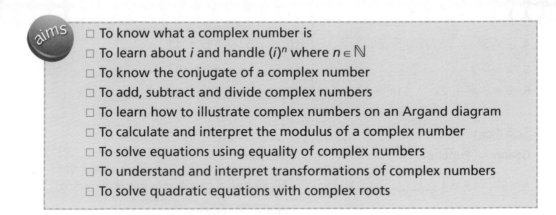

8 Complex Numbers

A **complex number** z, is a number of the form $a + ib$, where $a, b \in \mathbb{R}$ and $i = \sqrt{-1}$.

a is called the real part of z, written $Re(z)$, and

b is called the imaginary part of z, written $Im(z)$.

We say $z = a + ib$ is written in rectangular form.

Example

Express each of the following in the form ki, where $k \in \mathbb{N}$.

(i) $\sqrt{-16}$ (ii) $\sqrt{-100}$ (iii) $\sqrt{-9}$ (iv) $\sqrt{-49}$

Solution

(i) $\sqrt{-16} = \sqrt{(16)(-1)} = 4\sqrt{-1} = 4i$

(ii) $\sqrt{-100} = \sqrt{(100)(-1)} = 10\sqrt{-1} = 10i$

(iii) $\sqrt{-9} = \sqrt{(9)(-1)} = 3\sqrt{-1} = 3i$

(iv) $\sqrt{-49} = \sqrt{(49)(-1)} = 7\sqrt{-1} = 7i$

key point

$i = \sqrt{-1}$

Addition and subtraction

To add and subtract complex numbers, combine the real parts and the imaginary parts separately.

Example

If $\mu = 2 + 3i$ and $V = 1 - 4i$, express each of the following in the form $a + ib$.

(i) $\mu + V$ (ii) $V - \mu$ (iii) $3\mu - 2V$

Solution

(i) $\mu + V$
$= (2 + 3i) + (1 - 4i)$
$= 3 - i$

(ii) $V - \mu$
$= (1 - 4i) - (2 + 3i)$
$= 1 - 4i - 2 - 3i$
$= -1 - 7i$

(iii) $3\mu - 2V$
$= 3(2 + 3i) - 2(1 - 4i)$
$= 6 + 9i - 2 + 8i$
$= 4 + 17i$

Multiplication

Multiplication of complex numbers is performed using the distributive law, with i^2 replaced by -1.

Example

Simplify $4i + 3i(2i - 5) + 8$ and express your answer in the form $x + iy$ where $x, y \in \mathbb{R}$.

Solution

$4i + 3i(2i - 5) + 8$
$= 4i + 6i^2 - 15i + 8$ (remove the brackets)
$= 4i + 6(-1) - 15i + 8$ (replace i^2 with -1)
$= 4i - 6 - 15i + 8$
$= 2 - 11i$

exam focus

Candidates regularly make mistakes when subbing in negatives.

Example

If $z_1 = 1 - 3i$ and $z_2 = -2 - 2i$, express each of the following in the form $x + iy$, where $x, y \in \mathbb{R}$.

(i) $z_1 z_2$ (ii) $(z_1)^2$ (iii) $iz_1 z_2$

Solution

(i) $z_1 z_2$
$= (1 - 3i)(-2 - 2i)$
$= 1(-2 - 2i) - 3i(-2 - 2i)$
$= -2 - 2i + 6i + 6i^2$
$= -2 - 2i + 6i + 6(-1)$ (replace i^2 with -1)
$= -2 - 2i + 6i - 6$
$= -8 + 4i$

(ii) $(z_1)^2$

$\quad = (1 - 3i)(1 - 3i)$

$\quad = 1(1 - 3i) - 3i(1 - 3i)$

$\quad = 1 - 3i - 3i + 9i^2$

$\quad = 1 - 3i - 3i + 9(-1)$ (replace i^2 with -1)

$\quad = 1 - 3i - 3i - 9$

$\quad = -8 - 6i$

(iii) $i z_1 z_2 = i(-8 + 4i)$ from part (i)

$\quad\quad\quad = -8i + 4i^2$

$\quad\quad\quad = -8i + 4(-1)$ (replace i^2 with -1)

$\quad\quad\quad = -4 - 8i$

key point

In complex numbers, we usually write the real part first, as in part (iii) here.

---

exam Q

Given that $i^2 = -1$, find the value of (i) i^8 (ii) i^7.

key point

Solution

(i) $i^8 = (i^2)\,(i^2)\,(i^2)\,(i^2) = (-1)\,(-1)\,(-1)\,(-1) = 1$

(ii) $i^7 = (i^2)\,(i^2)\,(i^2)\,(i) = (-1)\,(-1)\,(-1)(i) = -i$

$i^2 = -1$ and $i^4 = (i^2)\,(i^2)$

$\therefore\ i^4 = (-1)(-1) = 1$

We can use these two facts to simplify any power of i.

---

exam Q

$\mu_1, \mu_2, \mu_3, \mu_4 \ldots$ is a sequence where $\mu_n = i^n$ and $i = \sqrt{-1}$.
Evaluate $\mu_1, \mu_2, \mu_3, \mu_4$ and μ_5.

Hence or otherwise, evaluate S_5, the sum of the first five terms.

Solution

$\mu_1 = i\ = i$

$\mu_2 = i^2 = -1$

$\mu_3 = i^3 = (i^2)\,(i) = -i$

$\mu_4 = i^4 = (i^2)\,(i^2) = (-1)(-1) = 1$

$\mu_5 = i^5 = (i^4)\,(i) = (1)\,(i) = i$

Now $S_5 = \mu_1 + \mu_2 + \mu_3 + \mu_4 + \mu_5$, that is, the sum of the first five terms.

$\therefore\ S_5 = i - 1 - i + 1 + i$

$\quad S_5 = i$

The previous example is a typical exam question in that the successful solution requires the candidate to link knowledge from different sections of the course, in this case complex numbers with sequences and series.

The conjugate of a complex number

The conjugate of a complex number is the same complex number except change the sign of the imaginary part.

$\bar{z}$ is the symbol for conjugate,

e.g. $z = 2 - 5i \Rightarrow \bar{z} = 2 + 5i$ and $z = 2i - 4 \Rightarrow \bar{z} = -2i - 4$.

key point

For conjugate, it is always the sign of the complex part that is changed.

Example

Given $z = -3 + i$, evaluate:

(i) $z + \bar{z}$ (ii) $z\bar{z}$

Solution

$z = -3 + i \Rightarrow \bar{z} = -3 - i$

(i) $z + \bar{z} = (-3 + i) + (-3 - i) = -3 + i - 3 - i = -6$

(ii) $z\bar{z} = (-3 + i)(-3 - i)$

$\qquad = -3(-3 - i) + i(-3 - i)$

$\qquad = 9 + 3i - 3i - i^2$

$\qquad = 9 - i^2$

$\qquad = 9 - (-1)$

$\qquad = 10$

> The addition of a complex number and its conjugate is always a real number.
> The multiplication of a complex number and its conjugate is always a real number.

Division

To divide complex numbers, multiply the numerator and the denominator by the conjugate of the denominator or simply:

Multiply the top and bottom by the conjugate of the bottom.

Let $w = \dfrac{1 + i}{2 - 2i}$. Express w in the form $p + iq$, $p, q \in \mathbb{R}$.

Solution

$$\frac{1 + i}{2 - 2i} = \frac{(1 + i)(2 + 2i)}{(2 - 2i)(2 + 2i)}$$ (multiply the top and bottom by the conjugate of the bottom)

Multiplying the numerator (top part):

$$(1 + i)(2 + 2i) = 1(2 + 2i) + i(2 + 2i)$$
$$= 2 + 2i + 2i + 2i^2$$
$$= 2 + 4i - 2$$
$$= 4i$$

Multiplying the denominator (bottom part):

$$(2 - 2i)(2 + 2i) = 2(2 + 2i) - 2i(2 + 2i)$$
$$= 4 + 4i - 4i - 4i^2$$
$$= 4 + 4$$
$$= 8$$

$$\therefore w = \frac{1 + i}{2 - 2i} = \frac{4i}{8} = \frac{i}{2} = \frac{1}{2}i$$

Argand diagram

Argand diagrams are used to represent complex numbers graphically. The **horizontal** axis is called the **real** axis and the **vertical** axis is called the **imaginary** axis. This representation is called the coordinated plane or the complex plane.

Complex numbers are plotted in exactly the same way as points in coordinate geometry (see the Less Stress More Success book for Paper 2), on the x, y plane or the cartesian plane.

Let $z = 5 + 4i$.

Plot z and $\bar{z}$ on an Argand diagram, where $\bar{z}$ is the complex conjugate of z.

Solution

$z = 5 + 4i$

$\bar{z} = 5 - 4i$

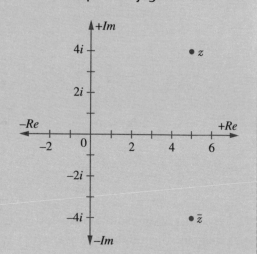

Notice that z is the image of $\bar{z}$ by axial symmetry in the real axis.

Example

$z_1 = 3$, $z_2 = -1 - i$, $z_3 = 2 - 2i$ and $w = 1 - i$.

(i) Evaluate $z_1 + w$, $z_2 + w$ and $z_3 + w$.

(ii) Plot $z_1, z_2, z_3, z_1 + w, z_2 + w$ and $z_3 + w$ on an Argand diagram.

(iii) Describe the transformation that is the addition of w.

Solution

(i) $z_1 + w = 3 + 1 - i = 4 - i$

$z_2 + w = -1 - i + 1 - i = -2i$

$z_3 + w = 2 - 2i + 1 - i = 3 - 3i$

(ii)

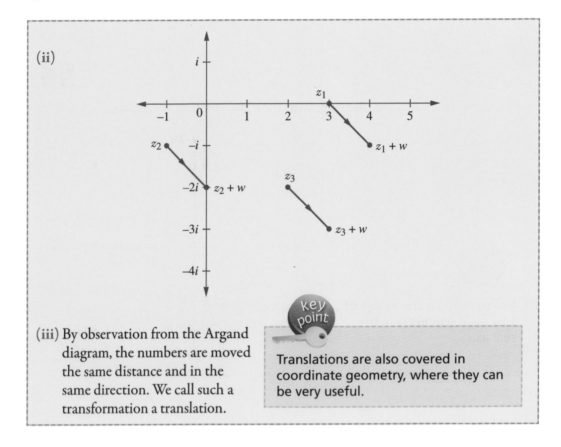

(iii) By observation from the Argand diagram, the numbers are moved the same distance and in the same direction. We call such a transformation a translation.

key point

Translations are also covered in coordinate geometry, where they can be very useful.

Modulus

The **modulus** of a complex number is the distance from the origin to the point representing the complex number on the Argand diagram.

If $z = a + bi$, then the modulus of z is written $|z|$ or $|a + bi|$.

The point z represents the complex number $a + bi$.

The modulus of z is the distance from the origin, o, to the complex number $a + bi$.

Using the theorem of Pythagoras, $|z| = \sqrt{a^2 + b^2}$.

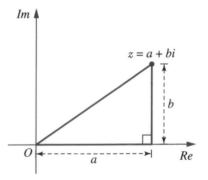

If $z = a + bi$, then
$$|z| = |a + bi| = \sqrt{a^2 + b^2}$$

Example

Find: (i) $|5 + 12i|$ (ii) $|3i|$ (iii) $|4 - i|$

Solution

(i) $|5 + 12i|$
$= \sqrt{5^2 + 12^2}$
$= \sqrt{25 + 144}$
$= \sqrt{169} = 13$

(ii) $|3i| = |0 + 3i|$
$= \sqrt{0^2 + 3^2}$
$= \sqrt{0 + 9}$
$= 3$

(iii) $|4 - i| = \sqrt{4^2 + (-1)^2}$
$= \sqrt{16 + 1}$
$= \sqrt{17}$

For what values of a is $|a + 8i| = 10$ where $a \in \mathbb{R}$?

Solution

$|a + 8i| = \sqrt{a^2 + 8^2} = \sqrt{a^2 + 64} = 10$
$a^2 + 64 = 100$ (square both sides)
$a^2 = 36$
$a = \pm 6$

Investigate if $|2 + 14i| = |10(1 - i)|$.

Solution

On LHS $|2 + 14i| = \sqrt{2^2 + 14^2} = \sqrt{4 + 196} = \sqrt{200}$ ①

On RHS $|10(1 - i)| = |10 - 10i| = \sqrt{100 + 100} = \sqrt{200}$ ②

Now compare ① with ②.

$|2 + 14i| = |10(1 - i)|$ is true, since $\sqrt{200} = \sqrt{200}$

Candidates are expected to know that when two complex numbers have the same modulus, those two complex numbers are equal distances from the origin, i.e. in the previous question, $2 + 14i$ and $10(1 - i)$ are equal distances from the origin.

The complex number $z =$ an $1 - 4i$, where $i^2 = -1$.

(i) Plot z and $-2z$ on an Argand diagram.

(ii) Show that $2|z| = |-2z|$.

(iii) What does part (ii) tell you about the points you plotted in part (i)?

(iv) Let k be a real number such that $|z + k| = 5$.
Find the two possible values of k.

Solution

(i) $z = 1 - 4i$
$-2z = -2(1 - 4i) = -2 + 8i$

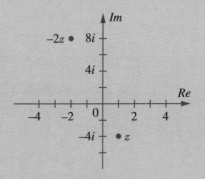

(ii) Notice ① $|z| = |1 - 4i| = \sqrt{1^2 + (-4)^2} = \sqrt{1 + 16} = \sqrt{17}$

② $2|z| = 2\sqrt{17}$

③ $|-2z| = |-2 + 8i| = \sqrt{(-2)^2 + 8^2} = \sqrt{4 + 64} = \sqrt{68}$

Now compare ② with ③.

$\Rightarrow 2|z| = |-2z|$ is true because

$2\sqrt{17} = \sqrt{68}$

$2\sqrt{17} = \sqrt{(4)(17)}$

$2\sqrt{17} = 2\sqrt{17}$ or from your calculator

(iii) Part **(ii)** tells us $-2z$ is twice as far from the origin as z.

(iv) Given $|z + k| = 5$ then:

$|1 - 4i + k| = 5$ (substituting $Z = 1 - 4i$)

$|(1 + k) - 4i| = 5$ (collecting the real parts together)

$\sqrt{(1 + k)^2 + (-4)^2} = 5$ (applying the rule for modulus)

$(1 + k)^2 + 16 = 25$ (squaring both sides)

$(1 + k)^2 = 9$ (subtracting 16 from both sides)

$1 + k = \pm 3$ (taking the square root of both sides)

$1 + k = +3$ or $1 + k = -3$

$k = 2$ or $k = -4$

Argument

The argument of a complex number z is the angle that the line joining the complex number to the origin makes with the positive side of the real axis. We use Arg (z) to denote the argument of z.

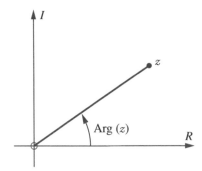

$z_1 = -1 + i$ and $z_2 = 1 + i$.

(i) Evaluate $z_3 = \dfrac{z_1}{z_2}$.

(ii) Plot z_1 and z_2 on an Argand diagram. Using a protractor, find the angles that z_1 and z_2 make with the positive side of the real axis, i.e. Arg(z_1) and Arg(z_2).

(iii) Plot z_3 on an Argand diagram.

(iv) Write down Arg(z_3).

(v) How is Arg(z_3) related to Arg(z_1) and Arg(z_2)?

Solution

(i) $z_3 = \dfrac{z_1}{z_2} = \dfrac{-1 + i}{1 + i} = \dfrac{(-1 + i)(1 - i)}{(1 + i)(1 - i)} = \dfrac{-1 + i + i - i^2}{1 - i + i - i^2} = \dfrac{2i}{2} = i$

$\therefore z_3 = 0 + i$

(ii)

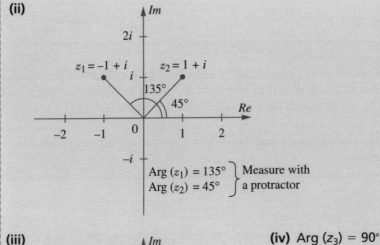

$$z_1 = -1 + i \qquad z_2 = 1 + i$$

$135°$

$45°$

Arg $(z_1) = 135°$ } Measure with
Arg $(z_2) = 45°$ } a protractor

(iii)

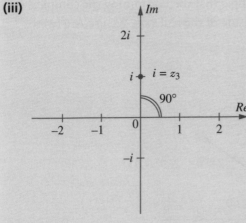

$i = z_3$

$90°$

(iv) Arg $(z_3) = 90°$
(by observation)

If z_1 and z_2 are complex numbers, then

$$\text{Arg}(z_1) - \text{Arg}(z_2) = \text{Arg}\left(\frac{z_1}{z_2}\right) \text{ and}$$

$$\text{Arg}(z_1) + \text{Arg}(z_2) = \text{Arg}(z_1 z_2).$$

(v) Arg $(z_1) -$ Arg$(z_2) = 135° - 45° = 90°$

∴ Arg$(z_1) -$ Arg$(z_2) =$ Arg(z_3)

exam Q

$z_1 = 4 - i$

(i) Find z_2 if $z_2 = iz_1$.

(ii) Plot z_1 and z_2 on an Argand diagram.

(iii) Describe the transformation that maps z_1 onto z_2.

(iv) Find z_3 if $z_3 = -iz_1$.

(v) Plot z_1 and z_3 on an Argand diagram.

(vi) Describe the transformation that maps z_1 onto z_3.

Solution

(i) $z_2 = iz_1 = i(4 - i) = 4i - i^2 = 4i + 1 = 1 + 4i$

(ii)

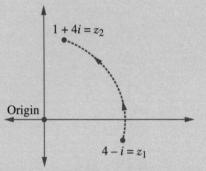

(iii) z_1 is mapped onto z_2 by a rotation about the origin of 90° anticlockwise.

(from the diagram in part (ii))

(iv) $z_3 = -iz_1 = -i(4 - i) = -4i + i^2 = -4i - 1 = -1 - 4i$

(v)

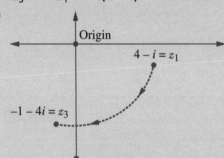

(vi) z_1 is mapped onto z_2 by a rotation of 90° clockwise.

(from the diagram in part (v))

key point

Multiplication by i always rotates a number 90° anticlockwise about the origin.
Multiplication by $-i$ always rotates a number 90° clockwise about the origin.

exam Q

Let $W = 2i$ where $i^2 = -1$. Plot **(i)** W **(ii)** W^2 **(iii)** W^3
(iv) W^4 on an Argand diagram.
(v) Make one observation about the pattern of points on the diagram.

Solution

(ii) $W^2 = (2i)(2i) = 4i^2 = 4(-1) = -4$

(iii) $W^3 = W^2 W = -4(2i) = -8i$

(iv) $W^4 = W^2 W^2 = (-4)(-4) = 16$

(v) From the diagram, it appears that the higher the power, the further away it is from the origin. Or you could say the points appear to spiral outwards in an anticlockwise rotation.

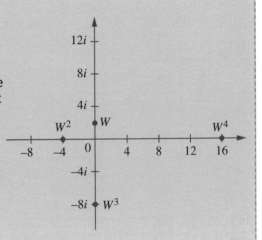

(i) Write each of the following complex numbers in the form $a + ib$ where $i^2 = -1$.

(a) $z_1 = \left(\frac{1}{2} + i\right)\left(\frac{1}{2} - i\right)$ (b) $z_2 = i^2 - i^3$

(ii) Which of z_1 and z_2 above is farther from 0, the origin on an Argand diagram? Justify your answer.

Solution

(i) (a) $z_1 = \left(\frac{1}{2} + i\right)\left(\frac{1}{2} - i\right) = \frac{1}{2}\left(\frac{1}{2} - i\right) + i\left(\frac{1}{2} - i\right)$

$$= \frac{1}{4} - \frac{1}{2}i + \frac{1}{2}i - i^2$$

$$= \frac{1}{4} - (-1)$$

$$= \frac{1}{4} + 1$$

$$= \frac{5}{4}$$

(b) $z_2 = i^2 - i^3 = -1 - (i^2)(i) = -1 - (-1)(i) = -1 + i$

(ii) $|z_1| = \left|\dfrac{5}{4}\right| = \left|\dfrac{5}{4} + 0i\right| = \sqrt{\left(\dfrac{5}{4}\right)^2 + 0^2} = \sqrt{\dfrac{25}{16}} = \dfrac{5}{4} = 1.25$

$|z_2| = |-1 + i| = \sqrt{(-1)^2 + 1^2} = \sqrt{1 + 1} = \sqrt{2} = 1.414$

Since $|z_2| = 1.414 > |z_1| = 1.25$, we can state that z_2 is further away from 0, the origin on an Argand diagram.

Candidates are not required to show the numbers on an Argand diagram in the above question. However, showing the numbers on an Argand diagram with no other work would probably get a partial credit in the exam.

Let $z_1 = 3 + 4i$ and $z_2 = 12 - 5i$.

$\bar{z}_1$ and $\bar{z}_2$ are the complex conjugates of z_1 and z_2, respectively.

(i) Show that $z_1\bar{z}_2 + \bar{z}_1 z_2$ is a real number.

(ii) Investigate if $|z_1| + |z_2| = |z_1 + z_2|$.

Solution

(i) $z_1 = 3 + 4i$ $\therefore \bar{z}_1 = 3 - 4i$

$z_2 = 12 - 5i$ $\therefore \bar{z}_2 = 12 + 5i$

$z_1\bar{z}_2 = (3 + 4i)(12 + 5i) = 36 + 15i + 48i + 20i^2 = 16 + 63i$

$\bar{z}_1 z_2 = (3 - 4i)(12 - 5i) = 36 - 15i - 48i + 20i^2 = 16 - 63i$

Now, $z_1\bar{z}_2 + \bar{z}_1 z_2 = (16 + 63i) + (16 - 63i) = 32$ which is a real number

(ii)

Take the left-hand side:	Take the right-hand side:
$|z_1| + |z_2|$	$|z_1 + z_2|$
$|z_1| = |3 + 4i|$	$z_1 + z_2 = (3 + 4i) + (12 - 5i)$
$= \sqrt{3^2 + 4^2} = \sqrt{9 + 16} = \sqrt{25} = 5$	$= 15 - i$
$|z_2| = |12 - 5i|$	$|z_1 + z_2| = \sqrt{15^2 + (-1)^2}$
$= \sqrt{12^2 + (-5)^2}$	$= \sqrt{225 + 1}$
$= \sqrt{144 + 25} = \sqrt{169} = 13$	$= \sqrt{226}$
So $|z_1| + |z_2| = 5 + 13 = 18$	$= 15.03329$

Since $18 \neq 15.03329$, we conclude that $|z_1| + |z_2| \neq |z_1 + z_2|$.

When looking for pattern in complex numbers remember:

If $|z| < 1$, then when a complex number is repeatedly multiplied by itself, it will spiral inwards (towards the origin) in an anticlockwise direction.

If $|z| > 1$, then when a complex number is repeatedly multiplied by itself, it will spiral outwards (from the origin) in an anticlockwise direction.

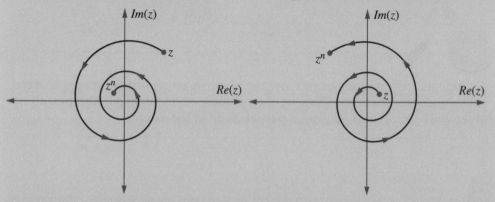

In the previous exam question we found the modulus of W by

$$|W| = |2i| = |0 + 2i| = \sqrt{0^2 + 2^2} = \sqrt{0 + 4} = 2 > 1$$

Hence $W, W^2, W^3, W^4 \ldots \ldots$ was an outward spiral.

Given $\mu = 3 - 2i$, plot the following on an Argand diagram:
$\mu, \ i\mu, \ i^2\mu, \ i^3\mu, \ i^4\mu$.

Make an observation about the pattern of points on the diagram.

Solution

$i\mu = i(3 - 2i) = 3i - 2i^2 = 2 + 3i$
$i^2\mu = -1(3 - 2i) = -3 + 2i$
$i^3\mu = -i(3 - 2i) = -3i + 2i^2 = -2 - 3i$
$i^4\mu = 1(\mu) = 3 - 2i$

$$|i\mu| = |i^2\mu| = |i^3\mu| = |i^4\mu|$$

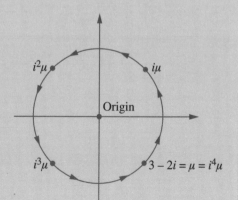

By observation, the pattern seems to form a circle.

exam focus

Notice the word 'seems' in the previous solution. In many questions, the examiner allows the candidate the freedom to express their opinion at certain stages. Full marks may be awarded for answers that are not strictly correct but 'seem' reasonable.

exam Q

Identify z_1, z_2, z_3, and z_4 on the Argand diagram using the following information:

  (i) $z_2 = \bar{z}_1$ **(ii)** $z_3 = iz_1$

(iii) $z_4 = 2z_1$

Solution

Label the points A, B, C, and D on the Argand diagram, as shown.

From (i) for B and C, one is the conjugate of the other.

From (ii), multiplication by i rotates the number anticlockwise $90° \Rightarrow B = z$, and $D = z_3$.

From (iii), A and B and the origin are in a straight line.
$\therefore$ A is a multiple of B
   hence $A = z_4$
Finally by elimination $C = z_2$

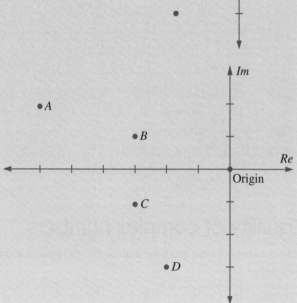

Z is the complex number $1 + i$ where $i^2 = -1$

(i) Find z^2 and z^3.

(ii) Verify $z^4 = -4$.

(iii) Using the value of z^4, or otherwise, find the values of of z^8, z^{12}, z^{16} and z^{20}.

z^4	z^8	z^{12}	z^{16}	z^{20}
-4				

(iv) Based on the pattern in part (iii) or otherwise, state whether z^{40} is positive or negative. Explain how you got your answer.

(v) Write z^{40} as a power of 2.

(vi) Write down z^{41}.

Here we see the topics complex numbers linked in an exam question.

Solution

(i) $z^2 = (1 + i)(1 + i) = 1 + i + i + i^2 = 1 + 2i - 1 = 2i$

$z^3 = zz^2 = (1 + i)(2i) = 2i + 2i^2 = 2i - 2$

(ii) $z^4 = z^2z^2 = (2i)(2i) = 4i^2 = -4$ (verified)

(iii) $z^8 = z^4z^4 = (-4)(-4) = 16$

$z^{12} = z^4z^8 = (-4)(16) = -64$

$z^{16} = z^4z^{12} = (-4)(-64) = 256$

$z^{20} = z^4z^{16} = (-4)(256) = -1{,}024$

key point

$16 = 2^4;\ 64 = 2^6;$
$256 = 2^6$ etc.

Hence

z^4	z^8	z^{12}	z^{16}	z^{20}
-4	16	-64	256	$-1{,}024$

(iv) From the table above $z^{40} = z^{20}z^{20} = (-1{,}024)(-1{,}024) = +1{,}046{,}576$

$\Rightarrow z^{40}$ is positive

(v) $z^{40} = 1{,}046{,}576 = (2)^{20}$

(vi) $z^{41} = z^{40}z = (1{,}046{,}576)(1 + i) = 1{,}046{,}576 + 1{,}046{,}576i$

Equality of complex numbers

If two complex numbers are equal, the real parts are equal and the imaginary parts are also equal.

For example, if $p + qi = x + yi$, then $p = x$ and $q = y$.

If one side of the equation does not contain a real part or an imaginary part, it should be replaced by 0 or $0i$, respectively.

Example

If $a + bi - 3 = 4i + 7$, find the value of a and the value of b.

Solution

$$a + bi - 3 = 4i + 7$$

Real   Real   Real

Real parts = real parts	i parts = i parts
$a - 3 = 7$	$bi = 4i$
$a = 7 + 3$	$b = 4$
$a = 10$	

Let $w = i - 2$.

(i) Express w^2 in the form $a + bi$, $a, b \in \mathbb{R}$.

(ii) Hence, solve $kw^2 = 2w + 1 + ti$ for real k and real t.

Solution

(i) $\begin{aligned} w^2 &= (i - 2)(i - 2) = i(i - 2) - 2(i - 2) \\ &= i^2 - 2i - 2i + 4 \\ &= -1 - 2i - 2i + 4 \\ &= 3 - 4 \end{aligned}$

(ii) Now solve $kw^2 = 2w + 1 + ti$:

$k(3 - 4i) = 2(i - 2) + 1 + ti$ (replace w by $i - 2$)

$3k - 4ki = 2i - 4 + 1 + ti$

Real   Real

Real parts = real parts	i parts = i parts	
$3k = -4 + 1$	$-4ki = 2i + ti$	
$3k = -3$	$-4k = 2 + t$	
$k = -1$	$-4(-1) = 2 + t$	(substitute $k = -1$)
	$4 = 2 + t$	
	$2 = t$	

exam Q

a and b are real numbers such that

$a(3 - 3i) - b(2 + i) = 3(1 + 2i)$.

Find the value of a and the value of b.

Solution

$$a(3 - 3i) - b(2 + i) = 3(1 + 2i)$$
$$3a - 3ai - 2b - bi = 3 + 6i$$

Real   Real   Real

Real parts = real parts i parts = i parts

$3a - 2b = 3$ ① $-3ai - bi = 6i$

                     $-3a - b = 6$ ②

Now solve the simultaneous equations ① and ②:

$3a - 2b = 3$ ①	Put $b = -3$ into ① or ②
$\underline{-3a - b = 6}$ ②	$3a - 2b = 3$ ①
$-3b = 9$ (add)	$3a - 2(-3) = 3$
$3b = -9$	$3a + 6 = 3$
$b = -3$	$3a = -3$
	$a = -1$

Thus, $a = -1$ and $b = -3$.

exam focus

In the previous question we see simultaneous equations from algebra linked with complex numbers. This is a typical exam-style question for our course.

Quadratic equations with complex roots

From your knowledge of algebra, you already know that the solutions to a quadratic equation, $ax^2 + bx + c = 0$, $a, b, c \in \mathbb{R}$, are given by the formula

$$x = \frac{-b \pm \sqrt{b^2 - 4ac}}{2a}$$ (see the booklet of formulae and tables, page 20).

In this formula, we refer to $b^2 - 4ac$ as the **discriminant**.

If $b^2 - 4ac < 0$, then the number under the square root sign will be negative and so the solutions will be complex numbers.

Verify that $4 - 3i$ is a root of $z^2 - 8z + 25 = 0$ and write down the other root.

Solution

$a = 1$

$b = -8$

$c = 25$

$\therefore z = \dfrac{-b \pm \sqrt{b^2 - 4ac}}{2a}$ gives us

$z = \dfrac{-(-8) \pm \sqrt{(-8)^2 - 4(1)(25)}}{2(1)}$

$z = \dfrac{8 \pm \sqrt{64 - 100}}{2}$

$z = \dfrac{8 \pm \sqrt{-36}}{2} = \dfrac{8 \pm \sqrt{(36)(-1)}}{2}$

$z = \dfrac{8 \pm 6i}{2}$

$\therefore z = \dfrac{8 + 6i}{2}$ or $z = \dfrac{8 - 6i}{2}$

$\therefore z = 4 + 3i$ or $z = 4 - 3i$

Hence, $z = 4 - 3i$ is verified as a root and the conjugate of $4 - 3i = 4 + 3i$ is the other root.

> **key point**
>
> An alternative method is to sub $z = 4 - 3i$ and check the equation is verified.

Let $z = 2 - i$ be one root of the equation $z^2 + pz + q = 0$
where $p, q \in \mathbb{R}$. Find the real value of p and the real value of q.

Solution

If $z = 2 - i$ is a root, then when z is replaced by $2 - i$ in the equation, the equation will be satisfied, i.e. LHS = RHS

$$z^2 + pz + q = 0 \quad \text{becomes}$$
$$(2 - i)^2 + p(2 - i) + q = 0$$
$$(2 - i)(2 - i) + 2p - ip + q = 0$$
$$4 - 2i - 2i - 1 + 2p - ip + q = 0$$
$$3 - 4i + 2p - ip + q = 0$$

Real parts = real parts	i parts = i parts
$3 + 2p + q = 0$	$-4i - ip = 0$
	$-4 - p = 0$
	$-4 = p$
$3 + 2(-4) + q = 0$	
$3 - 8 + q = 0$	
$-5 + q = 0$	
$q = 5$	

k is the line $x - y + 3 = 0$ and c is the curve $y^2 = 2x - 20$.
Prove that k and c do not intersect.

Solution

$x - y + 3 = 0$ and $y^2 = 2x - 20$

Get x on its own from the linear equation $x - y + 3 = 0$

$$\Rightarrow x = y - X$$

Then put in $(y - 3)$ for x in the curve $y^2 = 2x - 20$

$$\Rightarrow y^2 = 2(y - 3) - 20$$
$$y^2 = 2y - 6 - 20$$
$$y^2 = 2y - 26$$
$$y^2 - 2y + 26 = 0$$

Since $y^2 - 2y + 26 = 0$ has no obvious factors

we use $y = \dfrac{-b \pm \sqrt{b^2 - 4ac}}{2a}$

where $a = 1,\ b = -2$ and $c = 26$ to write

$$y = \frac{-(-2) \pm \sqrt{(-2)^2 - 4(1)(26)}}{2(1)}$$

$$y = \frac{2 \pm \sqrt{4 - 104}}{2}$$

$$y = \frac{2 \pm \sqrt{-100}}{2} = \frac{2 \pm 10i}{2} = 1 \pm 5i$$

Since the roots are complex there is no real solution.

This proves that k and c do not intersect.

This question has far more techniques from algebra than complex numbers.
Nonetheless, it is included here to illustrate, yet again, the linking of topics.
Overall, it is more likely to appear as a question in algebra.

9 Pattern I

Sequences

A sequence is a particular order in which related things follow each other. For example:

(a)  ?

(b)  ?

(c)

?

(d) 1, 3, 6, 10, **?**

Example

These four diagrams were made using matches.

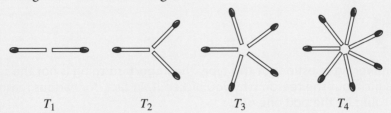

T_1 T_2 T_3 T_4

(i) Identify two different rules for the above pattern (sequence).

(ii) For each of the rules, draw the next diagram T_5 in the pattern.

(iii) Hence or otherwise, for each of the rules write down T_8, T_9 and T_{10}.

exam focus

Pattern questions may not always seem straightforward. It is important to try to visualise the problem. Some 'outside the box' thinking may be required.

Solution

(i) In numbers, the pattern is 2, 3, 5, 7.

What's going on?

Rule one could be nothing: the pattern simply repeats itself,

e.g 2, 3, 5, 7, 2, 3, 5, 7, ...

Rule two is 2, 3, 5, 7 . . . . . is the list of

prime numbers $\Rightarrow$ 2, 3, 5, 7, 11, 13, 17 . . . .

(ii) From part (i) above, the required diagrams are

Rule one

and

Rule two

(iii) By observation from the repeated pattern 2, 3, 5, 7, 2, 3, 5, 7, 2, 3, 5, 7, ...

$T_8 = 7$, $T_9 = 2$ and $T_{10} = 3$.

Again by observation from the list of primes 2, 3, 5, 7, 11, 13, 17, 19, 23, 29 . . . .

$T_8 = 19$, $T_9 = 23$ and $T_{10} = 29$.

Example

Which of these sequences is the odd one out? Justify your answer.

(i) $-3, -7, -11, -15, -19, -23, \ldots$

(ii) $1, 2, 3, 4, 5, 6, \ldots$

(iii) $2, 4, 8, 16, 32, 64, \ldots$

(iv) $1, 1, 2, 3, 5, 8, \ldots$

key point

When answering questions of this type, the important thing is not the sequence that you pick, but the reason why you picked it. In fact, for various reasons, they all could be the odd one out.

Solution

(i) Could be the odd one out because it is the only sequence with negative numbers.

key point

A sequence in which you go from term to term by adding (or subtracting) the same number each time is called an **arithmetic sequence** or linear sequence.

(ii) Could be the odd one out because it is the list of natural numbers, $\mathbb{N}$.

However, it is also an arithmetic sequence, with common difference $d = +1$.

(iii) Could be the odd one out because it is the only sequence that is geometric.

Multiply by 2 → Common ratio = $r = 2$.

key point

A sequence in which you go from term to term by multiplying (or dividing) by the same number each time is called a **geometric sequence** or an exponential sequence.

(iv) Could be the odd one out because it is the only sequence with a number repeated.

key point

A sequence where each number is the sum of the previous two is called a **Fibonacci sequence**, that is, $F_{n+1} = F_n + F_{n-1}$ with $F_o = 1$ and $F_1 = 1$.

Example

Match the following sequences labelled X, Y and Z with the given graphs P, Q and R and state the type of sequence in each case.

X: $3, -3, 3, -3, 3, \ldots \ldots$

Y: $43, 36, 29, 22, 15, \ldots \ldots$

Z: $5, 10, 20, 40, \ldots \ldots$

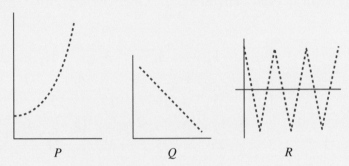

P Q R

Solution

$X \rightarrow R$ A geometric sequence with common ratio $= r = -1$
(value alternate $+$ to $-$)

$Y \rightarrow Q$ An arithmetic sequence with common difference $= d = -7$

$Z \rightarrow P$ A geometric sequence with common ratio $= r = 2$

key point

The graph shown could represent
(i) an arithmetic sequence with common difference, $d = 0$
or (ii) a geometric sequence with common ratio, $r = 1$.

Examples include $9, 9, 9, 9 \ldots \ldots$ $\boxed{\text{or}}$ $\dfrac{2}{3}, \dfrac{2}{3}, \dfrac{2}{3}, \dfrac{2}{3} \ldots \ldots \ldots$

Example

Row 3								
Row 4		1	4	6	4	1		
Row 5	1	5	10	10	5	1		
Row 6	1	6	15	20	15	6	1	
Row 7								

The pattern indicated above shows row 4, row 5 and row 6 of Pascal's triangle.

(i) Write down the pattern for (a) row 3 (b) row 7.

(ii) Given S_5 (the sum of row 5) $= 1 + 5 + 10 + 10 + 5 + 1 = 32$, calculate

(a) S_6 (b) S_8.

(iii) Write S_5, S_6 and S_8 as powers of 2. Hence write the value of S_9 as a power of 2.

(iv) Hence or otherwise, form a conjecture for S_n, the sum of the numbers in row n, and write down an expression for S_n.

Solution

(i)

Row 3				1	3	3	1		
Row 4			1	4	6	4	1		
Row 5		1	5	10	10	5	1		
Row 6	1	6	15	20	15	6	1		
Row 7	1	7	21	35	35	21	7	1	

(ii) (a) $S_6 = 1 + 6 + 15 + 20 + 15 + 6 + 1 = 64$

(b) $S_8 = 1 + 8 + 28 + 56 + 70 + 56 + 28 + 8 + 1 = 256$

(iii) By observation:

$S_5 = 32 = 2^5$

$S_6 = 64 = 2^6$

$S_8 = 256 = 2^8$

$S_9 = 512 = 2^9$

or

$S_9 = 1 + 9 + 36 + 84 + 126 + 126 + 84 + 36 + 9 + 1 = 512 = 2^9$

(iv) From part (iii) a conjecture (an unproven idea) could be that the sum of any particular row can be written as 2 to some power, in particular since $S_5 = 2^5$; $S_6 = 2^6 \ldots \ldots$

A conjecture is that $S_n = 2^n$ for Pascal's triangle.

exam focus

The word **conjecture** can appear almost anywhere in our exam. A conjecture can be considered an unproven mathematical theorem that may or may not be true. It is vital for candidates to have an opinion and write it down. Partial credits will be very easy to achieve in these situations.

Flow diagrams

This flow diagram will generate a sequence of numbers

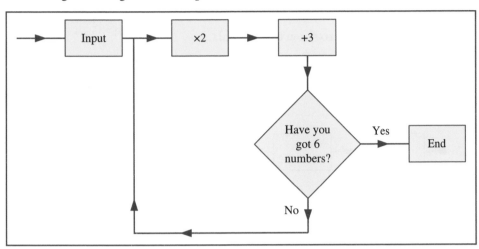

Starting with an input of $1\frac{1}{2}$, the flow diagram generates this sequence of numbers:

$1\frac{1}{2}$, 6, 15, 33, 69, 141.

The sequence is generated by using the first answer to generate the second and the second to generate the third and so on in a continuous loop.

This process is called an **iterative process**.

This diagram shows a simple iterative process.

Each output becomes the input for the next calculation.

Iterative processes have been known for thousands of years. However, with the introduction of computers their use has grown and they now have many different applications in mathematics and elsewhere.

The first output is called μ_1, the second μ_2, the third μ_3 and so on.

Using this subscript notation, the sequence generated is written:

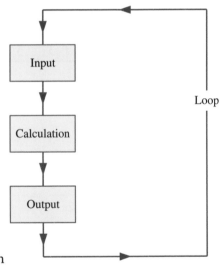

Loop

key point

μ_{n+2} means the $(\mu_{n+2})^{th}$ term and not $\mu_n + 2$.

Start $= \mu_1 = 1\frac{1}{2}$; $\mu_2 = 6$; $\mu_3 = 15$; $\mu_4 = 33$; $\mu_5 = 69$; $\mu_6 = 141$

key point

In terms of notation $\mu_1 = T_2$ and $\mu_2 = T_2$ etc.

Example

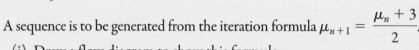

A sequence is to be generated from the iteration formula $\mu_{n+1} = \dfrac{\mu_n + 3}{2}$.

  (i) Draw a flow diagram to show this formula.

 (ii) Starting with $\mu_1 = 7$, generate a sequence of seven terms.

(iii) Suggest a possible limit of this sequence.

Solution

(i)

```
Input  →  +3  →  Divide by 2  →  Output
```

(ii) $\mu_{n+1} = \dfrac{\mu_n + 3}{2}$

$$n = 1 \Rightarrow \mu_2 = \frac{\mu_1 + 3}{2} = \frac{7 + 3}{2} = 5 \qquad (\mu_1 = 7)$$

$$n = 2 \Rightarrow \mu_3 = \frac{\mu_2 + 3}{2} = \frac{5 + 3}{2} = 4$$

$$n = 3 \Rightarrow \mu_4 = \frac{\mu_3 + 3}{2} = \frac{4 + 3}{2} = 3.5$$

$$n = 4 \Rightarrow \mu_5 = \frac{\mu_4 + 3}{2} = \frac{3.5 + 3}{2} = 3.25$$

$$n = 5 \Rightarrow \mu_6 = \frac{\mu_5 + 3}{2} = \frac{3.25 + 3}{2} = 3.125$$

$$n = 6 \Rightarrow \mu_7 = \frac{\mu_6 + 3}{2} = \frac{3.125 + 3}{2} = 3.0625$$

(iii) The sequence appears to be heading closer and closer to 3.

     We say the limit of the sequence is 3.

exam focus

The concept of a limit of a sequence or a function is part of our course. Limits may also appear in algebra, calculus and elsewhere. Candidates should develop the confidence to express an opinion in these situations. Whether your opinion is correct or not, you may be awarded the partial credit at least.

Example

The graphs, g and k, of two sequences are shown. One sequence is linear and the other is quadratic.

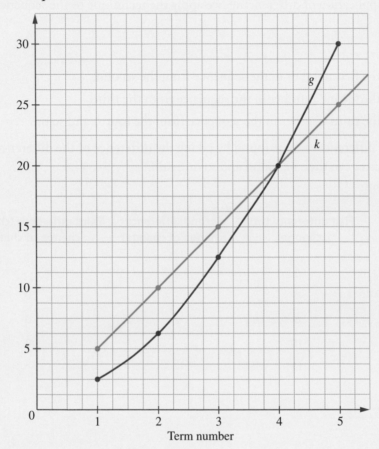

Term number

(i)   Identify the graph of the quadratic sequence and the graph of the linear sequence. Justify your answers.

(ii) Write down the first five terms of each sequence.

(iii) Evaluate S_5, the sum of the first five terms of the linear (arithmetic) sequence.

Solution

(i)   Observe k is a linear (straight line graph) sequence increasing by a fixed amount each time ($+5$, in fact).

Hence, g must be quadratic because it is not increasing by a fixed amount each time.

(ii) For k we write T_1, T_2, T_3, T_4, T_5 reading from the graph 5, 10, 15, 20, 25.

For g we write T_1, T_2, T_3, T_4, T_5 reading from the graph $2\frac{1}{2}, 6\frac{1}{4}, 12\frac{1}{2}, 20, 30$.

(iii) S_5 for $k = 5 + 10 + 15 + 20 + 25 = 75$

Differencing (change)

Many investigative and problem-solving questions lead to a sequence of numbers. The technique of differencing is useful in certain situations involving sequences. To observe an application of differencing, we apply the technique to the sequence 3, 7, 13, 21, 31, 43 . . . .

To do this:

- Subtract the first number in the sequence from the second.
- Subtract the second number in the sequence from the third.
- Subtract the third number in the sequence from the fourth and so on.

The **second** differences can be found by taking the difference of the differences. The third differences can then be found and so on again.

Hence we find:

	First difference (first change)	Second difference (change of change)	Third difference (change of change of change)
$\mu_1 = 3$			
	4		
$\mu_2 = 7$		2	
	6		0
$\mu_3 = 13$		2	
	8		0
$\mu_4 = 21$		2	
	10		0
$\mu_5 = 31$		2	
	12		
$\mu_6 = 43$			

key point

- When the first difference is the same value each time, the pattern is referred to as a **linear pattern**.
- When the second difference is the same value each time, the pattern is referred to as a **quadratic pattern**.

A quadratic pattern will be a curve and not a straight line.

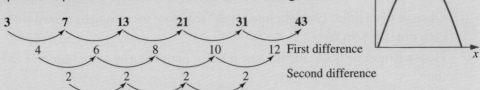

- When the third difference is the same value each time, the pattern is referred to as a **cubic pattern**.

Example

The Fibonacci sequence of numbers is 1, 1, 2, 3, 5, 8, 13, 21, 34, ...

Show that the sequence of first differences for the Fibonacci sequence is also the Fibonacci sequence.

Solution

Term	1	1	2	3	5	8	13	21	34

First difference (first change)	0	1	1	2	3	5	8	13

This new sequence is also Fibonacci .

key point

The second, (and all subsequent) differences are also the Fibonacci sequence in the above example.

To find the general term of a sequence with differencing

Example

Find the general term, T_n, of the sequence 7, 8, 11, 16, 23, ...

Solution

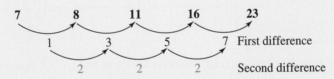

Because the second difference is constant, we know the pattern is quadratic.

$\therefore T_n = an^2 + bn + c$ where a, b and $c \in \mathbb{R}$.

In these situations, $2a$ = the second difference. You must remember this.

In this case we write: $2a = 2 \Rightarrow a = 1$.

We now have $T_n = 1(n^2) + bn + c$ and proceed to find the value of b and the value of c.

We use the first two terms to form two equations involving b and c and then use the method of simultaneous equations.

Given $T_1 = 7$ and $T_2 = 8$:

$T_n = n^2 + bn + c$

$T_1 = (1)^2 + b(1) + c = 7$

$\qquad 1 + b + c = 7$

$\qquad\qquad b + c = 6 \quad ①$

$T_2 = (2)^2 + b(2) + c = 8$

$\qquad 4 + 2b + c = 8$

$\qquad\qquad 2b + c = 4 \quad ②$

$-b - c = -6$	$① \times -1$
$2b + c = 4$	$②$
$b = -2$	
$b + c = 6$	$①$
$-2 + c = 6$	
$c = 8$	

Thus, $T_n = n^2 - 2n + 8$.

key point

You may check that $T_n = n^2 - 2n + 8$ is the appropriate formula to generate the given sequence 7, 8, 11, 16, 23, ... by substituting $n = 1, 2, 3, ...$

exam Q

The first four terms T_1, T_2, T_3, T_4 of a pattern are shown.

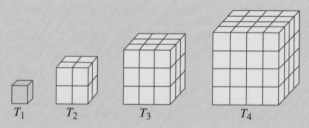

$\qquad T_1 \qquad\qquad T_2 \qquad\qquad T_3 \qquad\qquad\qquad T_4$

(i) How many cubes are in each of the next three terms of the pattern?

(ii) Use the first seven terms of the sequence to find the first difference, the second difference and the third difference.

(iii) Hence, explain why the sequence is cubic.

Solution

(i)

T_1	T_2	T_3	T_4	T_5	T_6	T_7
1^3	2^3	3^3	4^3	5^3	6^3	7^3

Hence, $T_5 = 125$; $T_6 = 216$; $T_7 = 343$.

(ii)

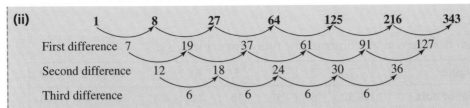

First difference 7   19   37   61   91   127

Second difference   12   18   24   30   36

Third difference   6   6   6   6

(iii) Since the third difference is the same value each time, the pattern is a cubic pattern.

exam focus

The word **hence** in the question of part (iii) forces us to use part (ii) when answering.

It is correct, simpler and more direct to state by observing the answers in part (i) that the sequence is cubic.

Example

In the following pattern, the first figure represents 1 dot, the second represents 3 dots, etc.

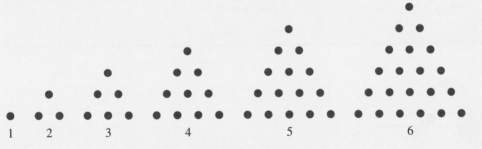

This pattern can also be described in function notation:

$f(1) = 1,$ $f(2) = 3,$ $f(3) = 6$, etc. where the domain is $\in \mathbb{Z}^+$.

  (i) Hence or otherwise, write down:

      (a) $f(4)$ (b) $f(6)$ (c) $f(7)$ (d) $f(10)$

  (ii) Write down the value of q where $f(q) = 78$.

(iii) Solve for x when $f(x) + f(x+1) = 64$.

Solution

(i) From the diagram we construct the following table.

Figure	1	2	3	4	5	6	7	8	9	10
Number of dots	1	3	6	10	15	21	28	36	45	55

Notice:

(a) $f(4) = 10$ (b) $f(6) = 21$ (c) $f(7) = 28$ (d) $f(10) = 55$

(ii) The pattern continues:

Figure 9   Figure 10   Figure 11   Figure 12
45   55   66   78

+10   +11   +12

$\therefore f(q) = 78$ means $q = 12$.

(iii) $f(x) + f(x + 1)$ represent two consecutive figures.
We write the sequence $1, 3, 6, 10, 15, 21, 28, 36, 45, \ldots\ldots\ldots$
and by trial and improvement find $28 + 36 = 64$.
$\Rightarrow f(7) + f(8) = 64$
$\Rightarrow f(x) + f(x + 1) = 64$ Answer $x = 7$

Once again, we see a question where topics are interlinked. The question and solution are relatively simple. However, the candidate must be familiar with the function notation and apply it to this straightforward pattern.

Example

The factors of the number 6 are 1, 2, 3 and 6.
The sum of these factors is $1 + 2 + 3 + 6 = 12$.
This fact is written as $\Sigma(6) = 12$.

In a similar way, the sum of the factors of 3 is:

$1 + 3 = 4$, so $\Sigma(3) = 4$.

And the sum of the factors of 8 is:

$1 + 2 + 4 + 8 = 15$, so $\Sigma(8) = 15$.

For any positive integer, $\Sigma(n)$ is called the Sigma function.

(i) Show that $\Sigma(24) = 60$.

(ii) Find $\Sigma(6) \times \Sigma(4)$.

(iii) Find $\Sigma(8) \times \Sigma(3)$.

(iv) Hence, investigate if

    (a) $\Sigma(6) \times \Sigma(4) = \Sigma(24)$ (b) $\Sigma(3) \times \Sigma(8) = \Sigma(24)$

(v) By considering any two prime numbers, find their sigma function value.

(vi) For any prime number y, write $\Sigma(y)$ in terms of y.

Solution

(i) The factors of the number 24 are 1, 2, 3, 4, 6, 8, 12 and 24.

    The sum of these factors is $1 + 2 + 3 + 4 + 6 + 8 + 12 + 24 = 60$.

    Hence, $\Sigma(24) = 60$.

(ii) The factors of the number 4 are 1, 2, 4.

    The sum of these factors is $1 + 2 + 4 = 7$.

    Hence, $\Sigma(4) = 7$.

    We were given $\Sigma(6) = 12$.

    $\therefore \Sigma(6) \times \Sigma(4) = 12 \times 7 = 84$

(iii) Given $\Sigma(8) = 15$ and $\Sigma(3) = 4$, we write

    $\Sigma(8) \times \Sigma(3) = 15 \times 4 = 60$.

(iv) (a) Investigate if $\Sigma(6) \times \Sigma(4) = \Sigma(24)$.

$$12 \times 7 = 60$$
$$84 \qquad \neq 60 \qquad \therefore \text{ Not true.}$$

    (b) Investigate if $\Sigma(8) \times \Sigma(3) = \Sigma(24)$.

$$15 \times 4 = 60$$
$$60 \qquad = 60 \qquad \text{Yes, is true.}$$

(v) Consider the prime number 19.

    The factors of the number 19 are 1, 19.

    The sum of these factors is $1 + 19 = 20$.

    Hence, $\Sigma(19) = 20$.

Consider the prime number 13.

The factors of the number 13 are 1, 13.

The sum of these factors is $1 + 13 = 14$.

Hence, $\Sigma(13) = 14$.

(vi) Now consider the prime number y.

The factors of the prime number y are $1, y$.

The sum of these factors is $1 + y$.

Hence, $\Sigma(y) = 1 + y$.

Part (vi) above could have asked:

Form a conjecture for Σy where y is a prime number.

- The solution as given in part (vi) above would be correct.
- Trial and improvement of any prime number should see at least a partial credit awarded.
- You must know what a conjecture is.
- Write something down, do not leave a blank space.

10 Pattern II

Arithmetic sequences and series

An example of an arithmetic **sequence** is 8, 11, 14, 17, ...

An example of an arithmetic **series** is $8 + 11 + 14 + 17 + ...$

It is vital to know the difference between a sequence and a series.

$\mu_n = T_n$ is the nth term.

S_n is the sum of the first n terms.

The general form of an arithmetic sequence is written as:

$$a \quad a + d \quad a + 2d \quad a + 3d \quad a + 4d \quad a + 5d$$

with a = first term = $\mu_1 = T_1$ and d = common difference.

key point

1. $T_n = a + (n - 1)d$

2. $S_n = \dfrac{n}{2}[2a + (n - 1)d]$ } in book of formulae and tables, page 22

3. $T_n - T_{n-1} =$ constant $= d$. This may be used to verify that a sequence is arithmetic.

4. If three terms, T_n, T_{n+1}, T_{n+2}, are in arithmetic sequence, then:
   $T_{n+2} - T_{n+1} = T_{n+1} - T_n$.

5. T_n may be determined from S_n by the rule $T_n = S_n - S_{n-1}$.

An arithmetic sequence is said to have a linear pattern. That is to say, the first difference, d, is the same value each time.

Example

Evaluate $\sum_{r=1}^{4} (3n + 5)$.

Solution

$$\sum_{r=1}^{4} (3n + 5) = [3(1) + 5] + [3(2) + 5] + [3(3) + 5] + [3(4) + 5]$$

$$= 8 + 11 + 14 + 17 = 50$$

The population of a type of insect is known to be 250,000 on 1 January in a particular year. Each month the population increases by 80,000. Find:

(i) The total population on 1 January the following year

(ii) The month in which the population exceeds $7 \cdot 2 \times 10^5$

Solution

The growth can be modelled by an arithmetic sequence with first term $a = 250,000$ and common difference $d = 80,000$.

(i) For the population at the start of each month, use the formula $T_n = a + (n - 1)d$.

key point

$T_1 =$ Jan 1st

$T_2 =$ Feb 1st etc.

To calculate T_{13} $\Rightarrow$ $T_{13} = a + (13 - 1)d$

$$T_{13} = 250{,}000 + 12(80{,}000) = 1{,}210{,}000$$

(ii) $7{\cdot}2 \times 10^5 = 72{,}000$

$$T_n = 250{,}000 + (n - 1)\,80{,}000$$
$$720{,}000 = 250{,}000 + (n - 1)\,80{,}000$$
$$470{,}000 = 80{,}000n - 80{,}000$$
$$6{\cdot}875 = n$$

Hence, the population exceeds $7{\cdot}2 \times 10^5$ during June i.e. before July 1st.

The first four terms of an arithmetic sequence are given as

$\quad a, -4, b, 6 \ldots$

Find: **(i)** The value of a and the value of b

$\qquad$ **(ii)** S_5, the sum of the first five terms

Solution

(i)

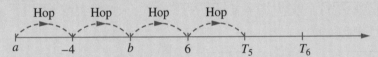

From the diagram, we observe that

travelling from -4 to 6 is two 'hops',

that is, a distance of $10 = 2d$

$$\Rightarrow 5 = d.$$

key point

From the diagram, each 'Hop' $= +d$.

Hence:

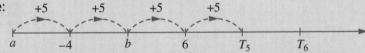

Becomes

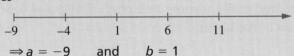

$\Rightarrow a = -9 \quad$ and $\quad b = 1$

(ii) $S_5 = T_1 + T_2 + T_3 + T_4 + T_5 = -9 - 4 + 1 + 6 + 11 = 5$

The first three terms in an arithmetic sequence are
$k + 6, 2k + 1, k + 18$.

Calculate the value of k and write down the first three terms.

Solution

We use the fact that in an arithmetic sequence, the difference between any two consecutive terms is always the same. We are given the first three terms.

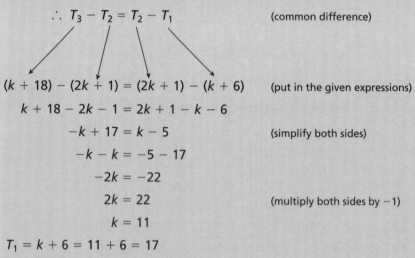

$$\therefore T_3 - T_2 = T_2 - T_1 \qquad \text{(common difference)}$$

$(k + 18) - (2k + 1) = (2k + 1) - (k + 6)$ (put in the given expressions)

$k + 18 - 2k - 1 = 2k + 1 - k - 6$

$-k + 17 = k - 5$ (simplify both sides)

$-k - k = -5 - 17$

$-2k = -22$

$2k = 22$ (multiply both sides by -1)

$k = 11$

$T_1 = k + 6 = 11 + 6 = 17$

$T_2 = 2k + 1 = 2(11) + 1 = 22 + 1 = 23$

$T_3 = k + 18 = 11 + 18 = 29$

Thus, the first three terms are 17, 23, 29.

Example

Ten markers are placed on the ground in a straight line at intervals of 8 metres. During a training session, a player, 8 m from the first marker, has to run to the first marker and back to the start, then run to the second marker and back to the start, and so on in succession until she runs to the tenth marker and back. Calculate the total distance run by the player.

Solution

Diagram

The player runs to the first marker and back. This is a distance of 16 m.

To the second marker and back, the distance is 32 m and so on.

Thus, the total distance run is given by:

$$16 + 32 + 48 + 64 + 80 + 96 + 112 + 128 + 144 + 160 = 880 \text{ m}$$

Alternatively, this is an arithmetic series where $a = 16$ and $d = 16$, $n = 10$ and we require S_{10}.

$$S_n = \frac{n}{2}[2a + (n - 1)d]$$

$$S_{10} = \frac{10}{2}[2(16) + (10 - 1)16] \quad (a = 16, d = 16, n = 10)$$

$$= 5[32 + 144]$$

$$= 5[176]$$

$$= 880 \text{ m}$$

In the first month after opening, a mobile phone shop sold 300 phones.

A model for future trading assumes that sales will increase by x phones per month for the next 35 months so that $(300 + x)$ phones will be sold in the second month, $(300 + 2x)$ in the third month and so on. Using this model with $x = 7$, calculate:

(i) The number of phones sold in the 36th month

(ii) The total number of phones sold over the 36 months

(iii) The shop sets a sales target of 20, 000 phones to be sold over the 36 months. Using the same model, calculate the least value of x required to achieve this target.

Solution

(i) The model indicates that in the 36th month, $(300 + 35x)$ phones will be sold. Put $x = 7$ into $300 + 35(x) = 300 + 35(7) = 300 + 245 = 545$ phones.

(ii)

First month	Second month	Third month	Fourth month
300	$300 + x$	$300 + 2x$	$300 + 3x$

The first term $= a = 300$.

The common difference $= d = x = 7$.

The number of terms $= n = 36$.

key point

The monthly sales follow an arithmetic pattern.

We now use $S_n = \frac{n}{2}[2a + (n - 1)d]$ and put in the above values.

$$S_{36} = \frac{36}{2}[2(300) + (36 - 1)(7)] = 18[600 + 245] = 15{,}210$$

(iii) Target of 20,000 $\Rightarrow S_n = 20,000$

$$\therefore \frac{n}{2}[2a + (n - 1)d] = 20,000 \text{ when } a = 300, n = 36 \text{ and } d \text{ is unknown.}$$

$$\frac{36}{2}[2(300) + (36 - 1)d] = 20,000$$

$$18[600 + 35d] = 20,000$$

$$10,800 + 630d = 20,000$$

$$630d = 9,200$$

$$d = 14{\cdot}603\ldots\ldots\ldots\ldots$$

$\Rightarrow$ In the model, $x = 15$ to achieve the target.

The pattern in the previous question is
(1, 300), (2, 307), (3, 314), (4, 321), (5, 328), ...
Plotting the points, we get:

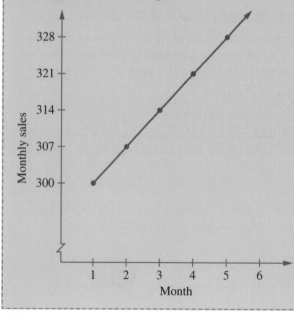

From the graph we observe that the pattern is linear and the rate of change is 7.
7 is also the slope or the common difference.
The examiner can easily link slope, common difference and rate of change in a question.

In an arithmetic sequence, the fifth term is −18 and the tenth term is 12.

 (i) Find the first term and the common difference.
 (ii) Find the sum of the first 15 terms of the sequence.

Solution

(i) Use $\qquad T_n = a + (n - 1)d$ twice to get:

$$T_5 = a + 4d = -18$$

and $\qquad T_{10} = a + 9d = 12$

Subtracting $\Rightarrow \qquad -5d = -30$

$$\therefore d = 6 \text{ and } a = -42.$$

(ii) Use $S_n = \dfrac{n}{2}[2a + (n - 1)d]$

$$\therefore S_{15} = \frac{15}{2}[2(-42) + (15 - 1)(6)]$$

$$S_{15} = \frac{15}{2}[-84 + (14)(6)] = \frac{15}{2}[0] = 0$$

exam focus

Once again, we require the skill to interlink topics, in this case simultaneous equations from algebra linking with sequences.

key point

This sequence of 15 terms is symmetric about zero.

$T_1 \quad T_2 \quad T_3$ $\qquad\qquad\qquad\qquad\qquad\qquad T_{14} \quad T_{15}$

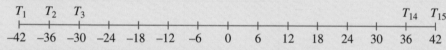

$-42 \quad -36 \quad -30 \quad -24 \quad -18 \quad -12 \quad -6 \quad 0 \quad 6 \quad 12 \quad 18 \quad 24 \quad 30 \quad 36 \quad 42$

When the 15 terms are added up, we observe $S_{15} = 0$.

exam Q

Lucy is arranging 1 cent and 5 cent coins in rows. The pattern of coins in each row is as shown below.

Row 1

Row 2

Row 3

Row 4

Row 5

(i) Draw the next row of coins, row 5, continuing the same pattern.

Solution

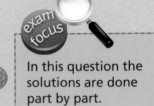

Row 5

In this question the solutions are done part by part.

(ii) The table below gives the number of coins and the total value of the coins in each row. Complete the table for rows 4 to 7.

Row number n	Number of 1 cent coins	Number of 5 cent coins	Total number of coins in the row	Total value of the coins in the row
1	1	0	1	1
2	1	2	3	11
3	3	2	5	13
4				
5				
6				
7				

Solution

Row number n	Number of 1 cent coins	Number of 5 cent coins	Total number of coins in the row	Total value of the coins in the row
1	1	0	1	1
2	1	2	3	11
3	3	2	5	13
4	3	4	7	23
5	5	4	9	25
6	5	6	11	35
7	7	6	13	37

(iii) Complete the following sentences to state, in terms of n, the number of 1 cent and 5 cent coins in row n.

(a) If n is odd, row n has _____ 1 cent coins and _____ 5 cent coins.

(b) If n is even, row n has _____ 1 cent coins and _____ 5 cent coins.

Solution

(a) If n is odd, row n has (n) 1 cent coins and $(n - 1)$ 5 cent coins

(b) If n is even, row n has $(n - 1)$ 1 cent coins and (n) 5 cent coins.

(iv) Find the total number of coins in the 40th row.

Solution

40th row $\Rightarrow n$ is even.

Hence, there are $(40 - 1)$ 1 cent coins and (40) 5 cent coins.

39 coins + 40 coins = 79 coins.

(v) Find the total value of the coins in the 40th row.

Solution

From part **(iv)** 39 × 1 cent coins = 39 cents

$\qquad$ 40 × 5 cent coins = 200 cents

$\qquad$ Total: €2·39

(vi) Which row has coins with a total value of 337 cents?

Solution

A big question: is n odd or is n even?

We examine both cases.

If n is even, then:	If n is odd, then:
$(n - 1) \times 1$ cent $= n - 1$	$(n) \times 1$ cent $= n$
$(n) \times 5$ cent $= 5n$	$(n - 1) \times 5$ cent $= 5n - 5$
Total value $= 5n + n - 1$	Total value $= n + 5n - 5$
$337 = 6n - 1$	$337 = 6n - 5$
$338 = 6n$	$342 = 6n$
$56\frac{1}{3} = n$	$57 = n$
Reject as n is even	Correct answer

(vii) Find the total value of the coins in the first 40 rows.

Solution

The 40 rows may be considered as two sets of 20 rows.

First consider the sum of the odd rows:

$= $ Row 1 + Row 3 + Row 5 + $\cdots$ + Row 39

$= 1 + 13 + 25 + 37 \ldots$

Since this is an arithmetic series with 20 terms,

we use $S_n = \dfrac{n}{2}[2a + (n - 1)d]$

$\qquad (a = 1 \qquad d = 12)$

$\qquad S_{20} = \dfrac{20}{2}[2(1) + (19)(12)]$

$\qquad S_{20} = 10[2 + 228] = 2{,}300$ cents

Next consider the sum of the even rows:

$= \text{Row } 2 + \text{Row } 4 + \text{Row } 6 + \cdots + \text{Row } 40$

$= 11 + 23 + 35 + \ldots$

This is also an arithmetic series with 20 terms, so we use $S_n = \dfrac{n}{2}[2a + (n - 1)d]$

$\qquad (a = 11 \qquad d = 12)$

$\qquad S_{20} = \dfrac{20}{2}[2(11) + (19)(12)]$

$\qquad S_{20} = 10[22 + 228] = 2{,}500 \text{ cents}$

$\Rightarrow$ Total value of the first 40 rows $= 2{,}300 + 2{,}500 = €48{\cdot}00$.

It is worth noting that the marking scheme for the previous exam question, awarding a total of 50 marks, was as follows:

(i) 10 marks – very short and simple

(ii) 10 marks – with a minimum of 6 marks awarded for one relevant step in the solution. Very, very easy.

(iii) 5 marks

(iv) 15 marks – with a minimum of 8 marks awarded for one relevant step in the solution. A huge amount of marks for a very simple question.

(v) 5 marks

(vi) and **(vii)** 5 marks. Lots of potential time trouble for some candidates.

It's not worth it. These final difficult parts are almost worthless, mark wise, in this question. Look at the length of the solutions to **(vi)** and **(vii)**.

Remember: Keep moving through every part of every question.

Stick to your time budget.

Marking schemes vary from question to question and from year to year. They may award high marks for the last part and very few for another part. Do not make it your policy to leave out the last part of questions.

(i) Prove that the sum of the first n natural numbers is $\dfrac{n(n + 1)}{2}$.

(ii) If the sum of the first k natural numbers is 2,850, what is the value of k?

Solution

(i) Sum of first n natural numbers $= 1 + 2 + 3 + \cdots + (n - 1) + n$ is given by

$S_n = \dfrac{n}{2}[2a + (n - 1)d]$ with first term $a = 1$ and common difference $d = 1$

$S_n = \dfrac{n}{2}[2(1) + (n - 1)(1)]$

$S_n = \dfrac{n}{2}[2 + n - 1]$

$S_n = \dfrac{n}{2}(n + 1)$

(ii) $S_k = 2,850$ and $S_k = \dfrac{k}{2}(k + 1)$ from part (i)

$\therefore 2,850 = \dfrac{k}{2}(k + 1)$

$5,700 = k^2 + k \qquad$ (multiply both sides by 2)

$0 = k^2 + k - 5,700$

$0 = (k - 75)(k + 76)$

$\therefore k - 75 = 0 \quad$ or $\quad k + 76 = 0$

$ k = 75 \quad$ or $\qquad k = -76$

 Answer $\qquad\qquad$ Reject, not a natural number

Above we solve for k using techniques learned in algebra. The question links the two topics of pattern and algebra.

Geometric (exponential) sequences

An example of a geometric sequence is 4, 12, 36, 108, . . .

In general, a geometric sequence is written as

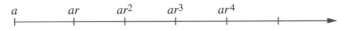

$$a \qquad ar \qquad ar^2 \qquad ar^3 \qquad ar^4$$

with $T_1 = a =$ the first term and $r =$ the common ratio.

key point

- $T_n = ar^{n-1}$ (In book of formulae and tables, page 22.)

- $\dfrac{T_n}{T_{n-1}} =$ constant $= r$. This may be used to show that a sequence is geometric.

- If three terms T_n, T_{n+1}, T_{n+2} are in geometric sequence, then $\dfrac{T_{n+2}}{T_{n+1}} = \dfrac{T_{n+1}}{T_n}$

exam focus

A geometric sequence, with common ratio r, is sometimes referred to as an exponential sequence.

exam Q

A flea is 160 cm away from a dog. It jumps towards the dog and with each jump it halves the distance between itself and the dog.

(i) Complete the table showing the distance between the flea and the dog.

Jump	0	1	2	3	4	5	6	7
Distance from the dog (cm)	160							

(ii) Plot a graph of the flea's distance from the dog against the jump number towards the dog.

(iii) Write down a formula for the flea's distance from the dog after *n* jumps.

Solution

(i)

Jump	0	1	2	3	4	5	6	7
Distance from the dog (cm)	160	80	40	20	10	5	2·5	1·25

(ii)

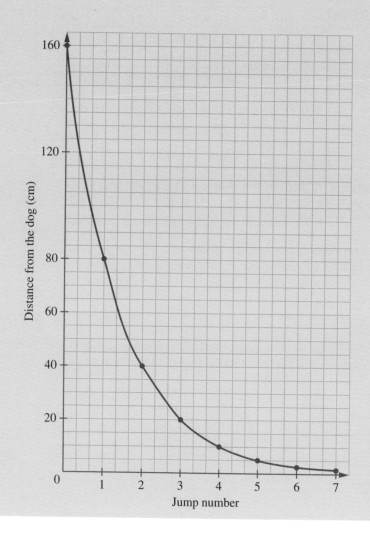

(iii)

Jump	Distance from the dog
0	160
1	$160 \times \dfrac{1}{2}$
2	$160 \times \dfrac{1}{2} \times \dfrac{1}{2} = 160 \times \left(\dfrac{1}{2}\right)^2$
3	$160 \times \dfrac{1}{2} \times \dfrac{1}{2} \times \dfrac{1}{2} = 160 \times \left(\dfrac{1}{2}\right)^3$
4	$160 \times \dfrac{1}{2} \times \dfrac{1}{2} \times \dfrac{1}{2} \times \dfrac{1}{2} = 160 \times \left(\dfrac{1}{2}\right)^4$
5	$160 \times \dfrac{1}{2} \times \dfrac{1}{2} \times \dfrac{1}{2} \times \dfrac{1}{2} \times \dfrac{1}{2} = 160 \times \left(\dfrac{1}{2}\right)^5$
6	$= 160 \times \left(\dfrac{1}{2}\right)^6$
7	$= 160 \times \left(\dfrac{1}{2}\right)^7$

Following the pattern in the table, we observe

$$T_n = 160 \times \left(\frac{1}{2}\right)^n$$

where n represents the jump number.

The first term of a geometric (exponential) sequence is 4 and the common ratio is 1·5. Write down the next three terms of the sequence.

Solution

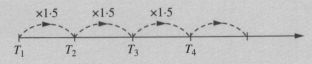

Hence, we get:

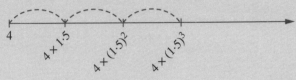

Answer $T_2 = 4 \times 1\cdot5 = 6$; $T_3 = 4 \times (1\cdot5)^2 = 9$; $T_4 = 4 \times (1\cdot5)^3 = 13\cdot5$

A new car is purchased for €45,000. The value of the car decreases (depreciates) at a rate of 15% per year. What will be the value of the car to the nearest €100 in

(i) 3 years' time   **(ii)** 8 years' time?

Solution

(i)

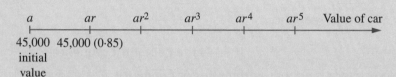

> After each year, the car's value is $100\% - 15\% = 85\%$ of what it was one year before. Hence, we have a geometric (exponential) sequence with
> $$r = \frac{85}{100} = 0.85.$$

In three years' time the value of the car is given by ar^3
$$= (45{,}000)(0.85)^3$$
$$= 27{,}635.625 = €27{,}600$$

(ii) In eight years' time the value of the car is given by ar^8
$$= 45{,}000\,(0.85)^3$$
$$= 12{,}262.07 = €12{,}300$$

The nth term of a sequence is given by $T_n = n^2 + 1$.

  (i) Write down the first three terms of the sequence.

(ii) Show that $T_1 + T_2 + T_3 = T_4$.

(iii) State if the sequence is geometric or arithmetic. Justify your statement.

Solution

(i) $T_n = n^2 + 1$
$$T_1 = (1)^2 + 1 = 1 + 1 = 2$$
$$T_2 = (2)^2 + 1 = 4 + 1 = 5$$
$$T_3 = (3)^2 + 1 = 9 + 1 = 10$$

(ii) $T_4 = (4)^2 + 1 = 16 + 1 = 17$

To show $T_1 + T_2 + T_3 = T_4$, put in the values from above:

$$2 + 5 + 10 = 17$$
$$17 = 17 \quad \text{True}$$

(iii) If sequence is arithmetic:

Then $T_2 - T_1 = T_3 - T_2 \ (=d)$

$$\Rightarrow 5 - 2 = 10 - 5$$
$$\Rightarrow \quad 3 \neq 5$$

∴ Not an arithmetic sequence.

If sequence is geometric:

Then $\dfrac{T_2}{T_1} = \dfrac{T_3}{T_2} \ (=r)$

$$\Rightarrow \dfrac{5}{2} = \dfrac{10}{5}$$
$$\Rightarrow 2\tfrac{1}{2} \neq 2$$

∴ Not a geometric sequence.

Hence the sequence is neither arithmetic nor geometric. The above work is my justification.

Part **(iii)** illustrates a technique sometimes employed by the examiner where neither of the given sequences are correct. You are not required in this instance to say that the sequence is in fact quadratic.

The first three terms of a geometric sequence are

$$2x - 4, \quad x + 1, \quad x - 3.$$

Find the two possible values of x.

Solution

$$
\begin{array}{ccccc}
a & ar & ar^2 & ar^3 & \text{Geometric} \\
\vdash & \vdash & \vdash & \vdash & \longrightarrow \\
2x-4 & x+1 & x-3 & &
\end{array}
$$

For geometric sequences $\dfrac{2nd \text{ term}}{1st \text{ term}} = \dfrac{3rd \text{ term}}{2nd \text{ term}} \ (= r)$

$$\dfrac{x + 1}{2x - 4} = \dfrac{x - 3}{x + 1} \qquad \text{(put in the given expressions)}$$

$\Rightarrow (x + 1)(x + 1) = (x - 3)(2x - 4)$ (multiply both sides by $(2x - 4)(x + 4)$)

$$x^2 + 2x + 1 = 2x^2 - 10x + 12$$
$$0 = x^2 - 12x + 11$$
$$0 = (x - 11)(x - 1)$$
$$\therefore x = 11 \quad \text{or} \quad x = 1$$

The solution ends at $x = 11$ and $x = 1$. However, the question could have asked you to find the two sequences. Then the following would be required:

a	ar	ar^2
$2x - 4$	$x + 1$	$x - 3$

For $x = 11$

$22 - 4, 11 + 1, 11 - 3$

$18, 12, 8$

a	ar	ar^2
$2x - 4$	$x + 1$	$x - 3$

For $x = 1$

$2 - 4, 1 + 1, 1 - 3$

$-2, 2, -2$

An application of sequences using $F = P(1 + i)^t$.

This formula is given on page 30 in the booklet of formulae and tables. We have previously seen in-context applications of arithmetic sequences, e.g. insect population, mobile phone sales. We now consider an in-context application with a geometric (exponential) sequence, in this case to model population change. Chapter 11 on arithmetic in this book applies geometric sequences to interest rates.

For growth/increasing situations, use $F = P(1 + i)^t$.

For depreciation/decreasing situations, use $F = P(1 - i)^t$.

Notice the information given about i on page 30 of the booklet of formulae and tables.

In January 2013 the polar bear population of the Arctic was estimated at 19,500. This population was considered to be decreasing – due to the loss of sea ice habitat caused by climate change – at a rate of 4% per annum.

(i) Given that this rate of decline continues, calculate an estimate (correct to the nearest one hundred) for the Arctic polar bear population in January 2024.

(ii) A study by the Arctic Watch Organisation suggests that by January 2056, the population of polar bears in the wild will be less than 500 individuals. Calculate the annual rate of decrease used by Arctic Watch to arrive at this figure. (Give your answer in percent correct to one decimal place.)

key point

From Jan 2013 to Jan 2024 is 11 years, $\therefore t = 11$ and the sequence is geometric. Use $(1 - i)$, as the rate is decreasing.

Solution

(i)

2013	2014	2015	2016	2017	2018	2019	2020	2021

$P(1-x)^0 \quad P(1-x)^1 \quad P(1-x)^2 \quad P(1-x)^3 \quad P(1-x)^4$

Now $\quad F = P(1 - i)^t$ where $P = 19{,}500$; $i = 4\% = 0{\cdot}04$ and $t = 11$

Becomes $\quad F = 19{,}500(0{\cdot}96)^{11}$

$\qquad F = 12{,}400$ to the nearest one hundred bears $\qquad$ (by calculator)

(ii) Again use $F = P(1 - i)^t$ where $F = 500$, $P = 19{,}500$ and $t = 2056 - 2013 = 43$

$\Rightarrow 500 = 19{,}500(1 - i)^{43}$

$$\frac{1}{39} = (1 - i)^{43} \qquad \text{(dividing both sides by 19,500)}$$

$$\left(\frac{1}{39}\right)^{\frac{1}{43}} = 1 - i \qquad \text{(Find the 43rd root of both sides)}$$

$0{\cdot}918329419 = 1 - i \qquad$ (by calculator)

$\qquad i = 1 - 0{\cdot}918329419$

$\qquad i = 0{\cdot}081670581$

$\qquad i = 8{\cdot}2\% \qquad$ (percentage correct to one decimal place)

That is to say, the Arctic Watch Organisation is using an annual rate of decrease of 8·2% to estimate the future population of polar bears.

Do not confuse i as a percentage with $i = \sqrt{-1}$ in complex numbers.

key point

Be very familiar with the potential of the calculator. When solving questions of the type shown above, a calculator makes the task simple and routine. The following example develops this skill.

Example

Use your calculator to find i in each of the following. (Give your answers correct to three decimal places.)

(i) $(1 - i)^{20} = 0\cdot49$ (ii) $(1 + i)^{18} = 1\cdot196$ (iii) $(1 + i)^{10} = 1\cdot877$

Solutions

(i) $(1 - i)^{20} = 0\cdot49$

$(1 - i) = (0\cdot49)^{\frac{1}{20}}$

Calculator $\downarrow$

$1 - i = 0\cdot965$

$0\cdot035 = i$

$3\cdot5\% = i$

(ii) $(1 + i)^{18} = 1\cdot196$

$(1 + i) = (1\cdot196)^{\frac{1}{18}}$

Calculator $\downarrow$

$1 + i = 1\cdot010$

$i = 0\cdot01$

$i = 1\%$

(iii) $(1 + i)^{10} = 1\cdot877$

$(1 + i) = (1\cdot877)^{\frac{1}{10}}$

Calculator $\downarrow$

$1 + i = 1\cdot065$

$i = 0\cdot065$

$i = 6\cdot5\%$

Example

Shrek goes on a diet. His weight, W kg, after t weeks is modelled by the formula $W = 150(2)^{-0\cdot01t}$.

(i) Find his current weight.

(ii) Find his weight, to the nearest kg, after

(a) 5 weeks   (b) 20 weeks.

(iii) Shrek's target weight is 135 kg. Using the method of trial and improvement, calculate the least number of weeks until Shrek gets below his target with this model.

(iv) Suggest a reason why this pattern may not continue.

Solution

(i) Currently $\Rightarrow t = 0$ $\therefore W = 150(2)^{-0.01t}$

$W = 150(2)^0 = 150(1) = 150 \text{ kg}$

(ii) (a) $t = 5$

$W = 150(2)^{-0.01t} = 150(2)^{-0.05}$

$W = 150(0.96593) = 145 \text{ kg}$

(b) $t = 20$

$W = 150(2)^{-0.01t} = 150(2)^{-0.20}$

$W = 150(0.87055) = 131 \text{ kg}$

(iii) Put $t = 10$ weeks into $W = 150(2)^{-0.01t} = 150(2)^{-0.1} = 139.95 \text{ kg}$

Put $t = 15$ weeks into $W = 150(2)^{-0.01t} = 150(2)^{-0.15} = 135.18 \text{ kg}$

Put $t = 16$ weeks into $W = 150(2)^{-0.01t} = 150(2)^{-0.16} = 134.25 \text{ kg}$

$\therefore$ After 16 weeks Shrek is below his target weight

(iv) • He gives up on the diet.

• The mathematical model does not apply after a certain number of weeks.

• He cannot continue to lose weight indefinitely.

We only need one reason. The answers given are not the only acceptable answers.

120° is the largest angle in a triangle. 7 cm is the largest side. The sides are consecutive terms of an arithmetic sequence. Use the cosine rule to find the length of each side.

Solution

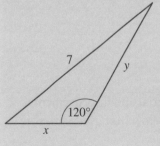

This solution requires techniques from sequences, trigonometry and algebra to arrive at a successful conclusion. A **classic** Project Maths type question.

Let the sides be x, y and 7 in ascending order.
Consecutive terms in an arithmetic sequence

$\Rightarrow 7 - y = y - x =$ common difference

$x = 2y - 7$

We now have the triangle:

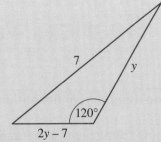

Apply the cosine rule: $a^2 = b^2 + c^2 - 2bc\,\text{Cos}\,A$

$$(7)^2 = (2y - 7)^2 + y^2 - 2(2y - 7)(y)\text{Cos}120°$$

$$49 = 4y^2 - 14y - 14y + 49 + y^2 - 2(2y^2 - 7y)\left(-\frac{1}{2}\right)$$

$$49 = 5y^2 - 28y + 49 + 2y^2 - 7y$$

$$0 = 7y^2 - 35y$$

$$0 = 7y(y - 5)$$

$$\therefore 7y = 0 \quad \text{or} \quad y - 5 = 0$$

$$y = 0 \quad \text{or} \quad y = 5 \text{ cm}$$

Reject   Accept

(Since $y > 0$)

To find x,

substitute $y = 5$ into $2y - 7 = x$

$$2(5) - 7 = x$$

$$10 - 7 = x$$

$$3 \text{ cm} = x$$

key
point

The question does not ask to check our answers. It is, however, instructive for us to do so here.

We now have the triangle:

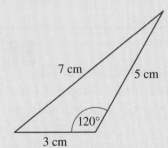

Are the sides in an arithmetic sequence?

Is $7 - 5 = 5 - 3$?   Yes ✓

11 Arithmetic and Financial Maths

aims

- ☐ To recap on aspects from the arithmetic section from Junior Certificate
- ☐ To learn how to calculate percentage mark-up, margin and loss
- ☐ To learn how to calculate relative error and percentage error
- ☐ To learn how to solve problems involving distance, speed and time
- ☐ To learn how to calculate compound interest and depreciation
- ☐ To learn how to calculate income tax

Revision of arithmetic material from Junior Certificate

At Junior Cert level you studied ratio and proportion, foreign exchange, household bills and percentages. The following are some questions involving this material.

Example

A train ticket now costing €28 is due to rise by 12% in a year's time. What will the price of the train ticket be in a year's time?

Solution

Find 12% of €28: $\dfrac{12}{100} \times 28 = €3{\cdot}36$ (this is the increase)

Cost of new ticket = €28 + €3·36

                = €31·36

Example

Chris has a mobile phone contract that gives him 100 minutes of calls and 120 text messages for a monthly charge of €25. Any additional calls are charged at 12c per minute and additional texts are charged at 7c per text. VAT of 22% is then added to all charges.

During the month of September, Chris made 132 minutes of calls and sent 174 text messages. Calculate Chris's phone bill for September.

Solution

Charges:

$$
\begin{aligned}
\text{Basic package:} \quad 100 \text{ mins} + 120 \text{ texts} &= €25{\cdot}00 \\
\text{Additional minutes:} \quad 32 \text{ mins} \times 12\text{c} &= €\ 3{\cdot}84 \\
\text{Additional texts:} \quad 54 \text{ texts} \times 7\text{c} &= €\ \underline{3{\cdot}78} \\
\text{Total (ex VAT)} &= €32{\cdot}62 \\
\text{VAT of 22\%:} \quad 22\% \text{ of } €32.62 &= €\ \underline{7{\cdot}18} \quad \text{(to the nearest cent)} \\
\text{Total due for September} &= €39{\cdot}80
\end{aligned}
$$

Example

Divide 238 in the ratio $2:5:7$.

Solution

1. Add up the ratios: $2 + 5 + 7 = 14$
2. Divide the total by 14: $238 \div 14 = 17$ (this represents one part)
3. Multiply by each ratio to find each part:
   1st ratio: 2 parts $2 \times 17 = 34$
   2nd ratio: 5 parts $5 \times 17 = 85$
   3rd ratio: 7 parts $7 \times 17 = 119$

A hotel website gives the cost of staying for three nights in a hotel in Copenhagen as 2,925 Danish kroner.

(i) Find the cost in euro, given that €1 = 7·5 Danish kroner.

(ii) This cost **includes** a 5% service charge for the website company. Find, in euro, how much the hotel will get for the three-night stay. Give your answer to two decimal places.

Solution

(i) Every 7·5 kroner is equal to €1, so we need to see how many times 7·5 divides into 2,925:

$$
\frac{2{,}925}{7{\cdot}5} = 390
$$

Therefore, 2,925 kroner = €390.

(ii) The cost of €390 includes a 5% service charge.

    105% = €390

    1% = €3·714285

    100% = €371·4285

    Therefore, the hotel will receive €371·43.

Alex's gas bill gave the following data:

Unit type	Present reading	Previous reading	Unit price
Day rate	42,384	40,932	€0.1702
Night rate	16,528	15,791	€0.0951

(i) Calculate the total cost of the units used, to the nearest cent.

(ii) Alex also pays a standing charge of €28·12 and a levy of €6·38. VAT is charged on all amounts. If the total amount of Alex's gas bill is €429·10, find the rate of VAT, to the nearest whole number.

Solution

(i) Number of units used = present reading − previous reading

Day rate	**Night rate**
Present reading: 42,384	Present reading: 16,528
Previous reading: 40,932	Previous reading : 15,791
1,452 units	737 units
× €0·1702	× €0·0951
Cost: €247·1304	Cost: €70·0887

Total cost of units: €247·1304 + €70·0887 = €317·2191 = €317·22

(ii) Charges:

               Units: €317·22

     Standing charge: €28·12

             Levy: €6·38

   Total of charges :   €351·72

     Total of bill = total of charges + VAT

        €429·10 = €351·72 + VAT

          €77·38 = VAT

$$\text{Rate of VAT} = \frac{\text{VAT}}{\text{Total of charges}} \times 100$$

$$= \frac{€77·38}{€351·72} \times 100$$

$$= 22\%$$

Example

A sum of money is divided between three people, Alan, Brian and Colm, such that Alan's share is twice that of Brian, and Colm's share is 50% of Alan and Brian's share together.

(i) Express the ratio of the sums of money received by Alan, Brian and Colm in its simplest form.

(ii) If Alan received €200, how much did Brian and Colm receive?

Solution

(i) Start by determining who receives the smallest share.

The question says Alan's share is twice that of Brian, and Colm's share is 50% of Alan and Brian's share together.

- Brian has the smallest share. Call this 1.
- Alan's share is twice that of Brian, so call Alan's share 2.
- Colm is 50% of Alan and Brian together. Alan and Brian together are 3, so Colm is 50% of 3. Therefore, Colm's share is 1·5.

$$\begin{array}{ccc} A : B : C \\ 2 : 1 : 1·5 \qquad \text{(multiply all parts by 2)} \\ 4 : 2 : 3 \end{array}$$

(ii) Alan received €200. This represents $\dfrac{4}{9}$ of the total sum.

$$\frac{4}{9} = €200, \text{ so } \frac{1}{9} = €50 \quad \text{(divide by 4)}$$

$$\text{Brian} : \frac{2}{9} = €100 \text{ and } \text{Colm} : \frac{3}{9} = €150$$

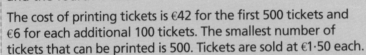

A raffle to raise money for a charity is being held.
The first prize is €100, the second is €85, the third is €65
and the fourth is €50.

The cost of printing tickets is €42 for the first 500 tickets and
€6 for each additional 100 tickets. The smallest number of
tickets that can be printed is 500. Tickets are sold at €1·50 each.

(i) What is the minimum possible cost of holding the raffle?

(ii) If 500 tickets are printed, how many tickets must be sold in order to avoid a loss?

(iii) If 1,000 tickets are printed and 65% of the tickets are sold, how much money
will be raised for the charity?

Solution

(i) The minimum cost of running the raffle must cover the sum of all the prizes
and the cost of printing the tickets.

Minimum cost = (sum of the prizes) + (cost of printing 500 tickets)

= (€100 + €85 + €65 + €50) + (€42)

= €342

(ii) The cost of the prizes and 500 tickets is €342 (from part (i)),
so the tickets sold must take in at least €342:

Minimum number of tickets = $\dfrac{€342}{€1·50}$ = 228 tickets

(iii) Cost of running a 1,000-ticket raffle:

Cost = (cost of raffle with 500 tickets) + (cost of printing 500 extra tickets)

Cost = (€342) + (€6 × 5)   [€6 per extra 100 tickets]

Cost = €342 + €30

Cost = €372

65% of 1,000 = 650 tickets sold

Income = 650 tickets × €1·50 = €975

Money raised for charity = income from ticket sales − cost

= €975 − €372

= €603

Percentage profit and loss

When selling an item, the seller can make a profit if the selling price is greater than the
cost price. Alternatively, the seller can make a loss if the selling price is less than the
cost price.

The percentage profit can be measured as a percentage of the cost price (mark-up) or the selling price (margin). The percentage loss is measured as a percentage of the cost price. The formulae are as follows:

		Percentage loss
Mark-up $= \dfrac{\text{Profit}}{\text{Cost price}} \times 100$	Margin $= \dfrac{\text{Profit}}{\text{Selling price}} \times 100$	$= \dfrac{\text{Loss}}{\text{Cost price}} \times 100$

It is very important for you to be aware of the subtle difference between mark-up and margin.

Example

A retailer bought 40 toasters at €22·75 each.
He sold 10 of the toasters at €34·99 each and sold the remaining
30 toasters at a reduced price. His total sales amounted to €1,315.

(i) Find his total profit on the transaction as a percentage of his cost. Give your answer correct to one decimal place.

(ii) Find the reduced selling price of each of the remaining 30 toasters.

Solution

(i) Cost $= 40 \times €22·75 = €910$
Profit $=$ total sales – total cost price
$= €1,315 – €910$
$= €405$

Percentage profit $= \dfrac{\text{Profit}}{\text{Cost}} \times 100$

$= \dfrac{405}{910} \times 100$

$= 44·5\%$

Note: This is known as the mark-up.

(ii) Let $x =$ selling price of the remaining 30 toasters.
Total sales $=$ (10 toasters at €34·99) $+$ (30 toasters at €x)
€1,315 $=$ €349·90 $+ 30x$
€965·10 $= 30x$ (subtract €349·90 from both sides)
€32·17 $= x$ (divide both sides by 30)
Thus, the 30 toasters were sold at €32·17 each.

An importer buys an item for £263·50 sterling when the rate of exchange is €1 = £0·85 sterling. She sells it at a 16% mark-up. Calculate, in euro, the price for which she sells the item.

Solution

Change £263·50 into euro:

Every £0·85 sterling is equal to €1, so we need to see how many times 0·85 divides into 263·50:

$$\frac{263·50}{0·85} = 310 \qquad \text{Therefore, £263·50 = €310.}$$

Profit is a mark-up of 16%:

$$\begin{aligned} \text{Profit} &= 16\% \text{ of cost price} \\ &= 16\% \text{ of €310} \\ &= 0·16 \times 310 \\ &= 49·60 \end{aligned}$$

$$\begin{aligned} \text{Selling price} &= €310 + €49·60 \\ &= €359·60 \end{aligned}$$

A retailer bought a consignment of DVD players for €12,000. He sold half of them at a 14% mark-up and the other half at a 20% margin. Calculate the total profit made and hence the total selling price.

Solution

$$\text{Mark-up} = \frac{\text{Profit}}{\text{Cost price}} \times 100 \qquad \text{Margin} = \frac{\text{Profit}}{\text{Selling price}} \times 100$$

$$14 = \frac{\text{Profit}}{6,000} \times 100 \qquad\qquad 20 = \frac{\text{Profit}}{6,000 + \text{profit}} \times 100$$

$$14 = \frac{\text{Profit}}{60} \qquad\qquad 20(6,000 + \text{profit}) = \text{profit} \times 100$$

$$\qquad\qquad\qquad\qquad 120,000 + 20(\text{profit}) = 100(\text{profit})$$

$$\qquad\qquad\qquad\qquad 120,000 = 100(\text{profit}) - 20(\text{profit})$$

$$840 = \text{Profit} \qquad\qquad 120,000 = 80(\text{profit})$$

$$\qquad\qquad\qquad\qquad 1,500 = \text{profit}$$

Total profit = €840 + €1,500 = €2,340

Total selling price = €12,000 + €2,340 = €14,340

Distance, speed and time

There are three formulas to remember when dealing with problems involving distance (D), speed (S) and time (T). Note: Speed here means average speed.

1. Speed $= \dfrac{\text{Distance}}{\text{Time}}$	2. Time $= \dfrac{\text{Distance}}{\text{Speed}}$	3. Distance = speed × time

Common units of speed

1. Kilometres per hour, written as km/h.
2. Metres per second, written as m/s.

Marks may be lost if you do not include units in your answers, where appropriate.

key point

It can be difficult to remember these formulae. To help you remember, consider the triangle on the right. By covering the quantity required, *D, S* or *T,* any of the three formulas above can be found by inspection.

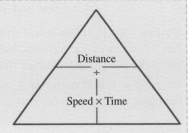

Distance
÷
Speed × Time

exam Q

Alice frequently travels from her home to Cork, a distance of 85 km. The journey usually takes 1 hour and 15 minutes.

(i) Find her average speed in kilometres per hour for the journey.

(ii) On a day of very heavy rain, her average speed on a 28 km section of the journey was reduced to 35 km/h. How long did this section of the journey take on that day?

(iii) How much longer did the total journey take on that day if she completed the rest of the journey at her usual average speed? Give your answer correct to the nearest minute.

Solution

(i) Convert 15 minutes into hours:

$$\frac{15}{60} = 0\cdot25 \text{ hours}$$

Distance = 85 km and time = 1·25 hours

key point

To **convert minutes to hours** divide by 60:
e.g. 24 minutes = 24 ÷ 60
$\qquad\qquad\qquad = 0\cdot4$ hours

$$\text{Speed} = \frac{\text{Distance}}{\text{Time}} = \frac{85}{1\cdot25} = 68 \text{ km/h}$$

(ii) Distance = 28 km and speed = 35 km/h:

$$\text{Time} = \frac{\text{Distance}}{\text{Speed}} = \frac{28}{35} = 0\cdot8 \text{ hours}$$

(iii) She spent 28 km travelling at 35 km/h, which took her 0·8 hours   (from part (ii))

She spent the rest of the journey, 85 km − 28 km = 57 km, travelling at 68 km/h.

$$\text{Time} = \frac{\text{Distance}}{\text{Speed}} = \frac{57}{68} = 0\cdot838 \text{ hours}$$

Total time = 0·8 + 0·838

         = 1·638

         = 1 hour and 0·638 hours

         = 1 hour and (0·638 × 60) minutes

         = 1 hour and 38·28 minutes

If Alice travels at her usual speed it will take her 1 hour and 15 minutes, but on this day it will take her 1 hour and 38 minutes.

Therefore, it will take her 23 minutes longer to make the journey on this day.

key point

To **convert hours to minutes** multiply by 60:

e.g. 0·3 hours = 0·3 × 60

                   = 18 minutes

exam focus

Note:

0·638 hours is **NOT** 63·8 minutes. This is a common error.

Relative error and percentage error

When calculations are being made, errors can occur, especially calculations which involve rounding. It is important to have a measure of the error.

Definitions

Error = | true value − estimate value | and is always considered positive.

Relative error = $\dfrac{\text{Error}}{\text{True value}}$

Percentage error = $\dfrac{\text{Error}}{\text{True value}} \times 100\%$

Accumulated error: the collected inaccuracy that can occur when multiple errors are combined.

Example

Four telephone calls cost €3·85, €7·45, €8·40 and €11·55.

(i) John estimates the total cost of the four calls by ignoring the cent part in the cost of each call. Calculate the percentage error in his estimate.

(ii) Anne estimates the total cost of the four calls by rounding the cost of each call to the nearest euro. Calculate the percentage error in her estimate.

Solution

(i) True cost of the phone calls: €3·85 + €7·45 + €8·40 + €11·55 = €31·25

John ignores the cent part of each value: €3 + €7 + €8 + €11 = €29

Error = |true value − estimate|

Error = |€31·25 − €29|

Error = €2·25

$$\text{Percentage error} = \frac{\text{Error}}{\text{True value}} \times 100$$

$$\text{Percentage error} = \frac{2·25}{31·25} \times 100 = 7·2\% \text{ error}$$

(ii) True cost of the phone calls: €3·85 + €7·45 + €8·40 + €11·55 = €31·25

Anne rounds to the nearest euro: €4 + €7 + €8 + €12 = €31

Error = |true value − estimate|

Error = |€31·25 − €31|

Error = €0·25

$$\text{Percentage error} = \frac{\text{Error}}{\text{True value}} \times 100$$

$$\text{Percentage error} = \frac{0·25}{31·25} \times 100 = 0·8\% \text{ error}$$

The speedometer in a car is faulty. When the car is actually travelling at 57 km/h, the speedometer reads 60 km/h.

(i) Calculate the percentage error, correct to one decimal place.

(ii) If the percentage error is the same at all speeds, at what speed is the car actually travelling when the speedometer reads 110 km/h? Give your answer correct to one decimal place.

(iii) The driver is not aware of the fault. He calculates that if he travels at an average speed of 80 km/h, as shown on the speedometer, he will reach his destination in four hours. How long, correct to the nearest minute, will it actually take him to reach his destination?

Solution

(i) Percentage error $= \dfrac{\text{Error}}{\text{True value}} \times 100$

$$= \frac{3}{57} \times 100$$

$$= 5 \cdot 3\%$$

(ii) The speedometer is showing a reading which is 105·3% that of the actual speed.

$$105 \cdot 3\% = 110$$

$1\% = 1 \cdot 04463$ (divide both sides by 105·3)

$100\% = 104 \cdot 46$ (multiply both sides by 100)

Therefore, the actual speed of the car is 104·5 km/h.

(iii) Based on speed = 80 km/h and time = 4 hours: Distance = (speed) × (time)

$$= (80) \times (4)$$

$$= 320 \text{ km}$$

Speedometer reading is 80 km/hr: $80 = 105.3\%$

$$0 \cdot 759734 = 1\%$$

$$75 \cdot 9734 = 100\%$$

Thus, actual speed = 75·9734 km/h.

Distance = 320 km and speed = 75·9734 km/h.

$$\text{Time} = \frac{\text{Distance}}{\text{Speed}} = \frac{320}{75 \cdot 9734} = 4 \cdot 212 \text{ hours}$$

$$= 4 \text{ hours and } 0 \cdot 212 \text{ hours}$$

$$= 4 \text{ hours and } (0 \cdot 212 \times 60) \text{ minutes}$$

$$= 4 \text{ hours and } 12 \cdot 72 \text{ minutes}$$

Therefore, it will take him 13 minutes longer to make the journey (to the nearest minute).

A factory produces cartons of juice, each carton contains one litre of juice. The machine which fills the cartons has a tolerance of 5 ml per 500 ml of juice.

  (i) Find the minimum possible volume per carton.

  (ii) Find the maximum possible volume per carton.

(iii) The cartons of juice are sold for €0·85 each. The machine is at its lower end of the tolerance level for a duration of 36 hours. If the machine can fill 5 cartons per minute, calculate the quantity of juice

and hence the amount of money that the factory saved during this 36-hour period.

Tolerance

When making measurements, there is often an allowable percentage error. The tolerance is the amount of error accepted in a given situation.

Solution

(i) If the machine is filling the cartons at the lower end of its tolerance level, it will be underfilling the cartons at 5 ml per 500 ml.

Therefore, a 1 litre carton would contain 990 ml.

(ii) If the machine is filling the cartons at the upper end of its tolerance level, it will be overfilling the cartons at 5 ml per 500 ml.

Therefore, a 1 litre carton would contain 1,010 ml.

(iii) 5 cartons per minute = 5 × 60 = 300 cartons per hour.

300 cartons per hour = 300 × 36 = 10,800 cartons for the 36-hour period.

If each carton is underfilled by 10 ml, the factory will save:
10 ml × 10,800 = 108,000 ml = 108 litres of juice.

Amount of money saved = 108 litres × €0·85 = €91·80.

Interest

Interest is the sum of money that you pay for borrowing money or that is paid to you for lending money.

When dealing with interest, we use the following symbols:

(see booklet of formulae and tables, page 30)

P = the **principal**, the sum of money borrowed or invested at the beginning of the period.

t = the **time**, the number of weeks/months/years for which the sum of money is borrowed or invested.

i = the **interest rate**, the percentage rate per week/month/year expressed as a fraction or a decimal at which interest is charged.

F = the **final amount**, i.e. the final sum of money, including interest, at the end of the period.

Note: per annum = per year.

Annual equivalent rate (AER) and annual percentage rate (APR) (both percentage rates). Investments: AER tells you how much your money would earn in exactly one year. Loans: APR tells you how much your loan will grow by in exactly one year.

Compound interest

When a sum of money earns interest, this interest is often added to the principal to form a new principal. This new principal earns interest in the next year and so on. This is called **compound interest**.

When calculating compound interest, do the following.

Method 1:

Calculate the interest for the **first** year and add this to the principal to form the new principal for the next year. Calculate the interest for **one** year on this new principal and add it on to form the principal for the next year, and so on. The easiest way to calculate each stage is to multiply the principal at the beginning of each year by the factor:

$$(1 + i)$$

This will give the principal for the next year, and so on.

Method 2:

If the number of years is greater than three, then using a formula and a calculator will be much quicker.

Use the formula: $F = P(1 + i)^t$

(see booklet of formulae and tables, page 30)

The formula does not work if: the interest rate, i, is changed during the period

or

money is added or subtracted during the period.

Therefore you must use method 1.

Example

€12,500 is invested in a savings account where the interest is compounded annually with an AER of 3·75%. Calculate the future value of this investment in five years.

Solution

The rate is not changing and no money was removed or added during the time period. Therefore, we can use the formula:

$P = 12,500,\ i = 0·0375,\quad t = 5$

$$F = P(1 + i)^t$$
$$F = 12,500(1 + 0·0375)^5$$
$$F = 12,500(1·0375)^5$$
$$F = 15,026·25$$

The €12,500 is worth €15,026·25 in five years' time.

Example

What sum of money invested at 4·6% per annum compound interest will amount to €3,130 in five years? Give your answer correct to the nearest euro.

Solution

The rate is not changing and no money was removed or added during the time period. Therefore, we can use the formula:

$F = 3,130,\ i = 4·6\% = 0·046,\quad t = 5,\quad P = ?$

$$F = P(1 + i)^t$$
$$3,130 = P(1 + 0·046)^5$$
$$3,130 = P(1·046)^5$$
$$\frac{3,130}{(1·046)^5} = P$$
$$2,499·68 = P$$

Therefore, €2,500 will amount to €3,130 in five years' time.

(i) A certain deposit account will earn 3% interest in the first year and 6% interest in the second year. The interest is added to the account at the end of each year. If a person invests €20,000 in this account, how much will they have in the account at the end of the two years?

(ii) Show that, to the nearest euro, the same amount of interest is earned by investing the money for two years in an account that pays compound interest at 4·49% (AER).

Solution

(i) Year 1: $P = 20,000$, $i = 3\% = 0·03$, $t = 1$

$F = P(1 + i)^t$

$F = 20,000(1 + 0·03)^1$

$F = 20,000(1·03)$

$F = 20,600$

Year 2: $P = 20,600$, $i = 6\% = 0·06$, $t = 1$

$F = P(1 + i)^t$

$F = 20,600(1 + 0·06)^1$

$F = 20,600(1·06)$

$F = 21,836$

The final balance after two years = €21,836.

(ii) To find the AER, find the value of i for which €20,000 will have a final value of €21,836 after two years:

$F = 21,836$, $P = 20,000$, $t = 2$, $i = ?$

$$F = P(1 + i)^t$$

$$21,836 = 20,000(1 + i)^2$$

$$\frac{21,836}{20,000} = (1 + i)^2 \qquad \text{(divide both sides by 20,000)}$$

$$\sqrt{\frac{21,836}{20,000}} = 1 + i \qquad \text{(square root of both sides)}$$

$$1·044892339 = 1 + i$$

$$0·044892339 = i \qquad \text{(subtract 1 from both sides)}$$

$$4·4892339\% = i$$

$$4·49\% = i$$

exam focus

Do not round off answers until the end of the question. Otherwise your answers won't be accurate.

(i) A sum of €5,000 is invested in an eight-year government bond with an annual equivalent rate (AER) of 6%. Find the value of the investment when it matures in eight years' time.

(ii) A different investment bond gives 20% interest after 8 years. Calculate the AER for this bond.

Solution

(i) $P = 5,000$ $i = 6\% = 0.06$ $t = 8$

$$F = P(1 + i)^t$$
$$F = 5,000(1 + 0.06)^8$$
$$F = 5,000(1.06)^8$$
$$F = 7,969.24$$

key point

A bond is a certificate issued by a government or a public company promising to repay borrowed money at a fixed rate of interest at a specified time.

Therefore, the €5,000 has a final value of €7,969.24 in eight years' time.

(ii) Different bond gives 20% interest after eight years:

$$20\% \text{ of } €5,000 = €1,000$$

Final value of €5,000 invested in this bond in eight years = €5,000 + €1,000 = €6,000.

To find the AER, find the value of i for which €5,000 will have a final value of €6,000 after eight years:

$$F = 6,000, \ P = 5,000, \ t = 8, \ i = ?$$

$$F = P(1 + i)^t$$
$$6,000 = 5,000(1 + i)^8$$
$$\frac{6,000}{5,000} = (1 + i)^8 \qquad \text{(divide both sides by 5,000)}$$

$$\sqrt[8]{\frac{6,000}{5,000}} = 1 + i \qquad \text{(find 8th root of both sides)}$$

$$\sqrt[8]{1.2} = 1 + i$$
$$1.023051875 = 1 + i$$
$$0.023051875 = i \qquad \text{(subtract 1 from both sides)}$$
$$2.3051875\% = i \qquad \text{(multiply by 100)}$$

Thus, the annual equivalent rate (AER) which is equal to receiving 20% interest at the end of eight years is $i = 2.3\%$.

key point

Use the $\boxed{\sqrt[\square]{\square}}$ function on your calculator to evaluate $\sqrt[8]{\dfrac{6,000}{5,000}}$, or $\sqrt[8]{1.2}$

€42,000 was invested for three years at compound interest. The interest rate for the first year was 6% per annum, the interest rate for the second year was 4% per annum and the interest rate for the third year was 3% per annum. At the end of the first year, €1,520 was withdrawn.

(i) Find the value of the investment at the start of the year two.

(ii) At the end of the second year €W was withdrawn. At the end of the third year the investment was worth €41,200. Find the value of W.

Solution

(i) $F = P(1 + i)$,　　　　　　$P = €42,000$,　　　　　　$i = 6\% = 0.06$

$F = 42,000(1 + 0.06) = €44,520$

　　　　Value at end of year 1:　€44,520

　　　　　　　　Withdrawn:　€1,520

　　　Value at the start of year 2:　€43,000

(ii) $F = P(1 + i)$,　　　　　　$P = €43,000$,　　　　　　$i = 4\% = 0.04$

$F = 43,000(1 + 0.04) = €44,720$

　　　　Value at end of year 2:　€44,720

　　　　　　　　Withdrawn:　€ W

　　　Value at the start of year 3:　€44,720 − €W

　　　　$F = P(1 + i)$,　　　$P = €44,720 − €W$,　$i = 3\% = 0.03$,　$F = €41,200$

$41,200 = (44,720 − W)(1 + 0.03)$

$41,200 = (44,720 − W)(1.03)$

$40,000 = 44,720 − W$　　　　　　　　　(divide both sides by 1.03)

　$W = 44,720 − 40,000$

　$W = 4,720$

Therefore, €4,720 was withdrawn at the end of the second year.

Depreciation

Over time, material goods (e.g. machinery, vehicles, etc.) lose value as a result of wear and tear, age or obsolescence. This loss of value is known as depreciation.

Reducing balance method

Using the reducing balance method, the cost of the asset is depreciated at a constant rate each year. This method is based on the principle that an asset is more useful in its initial years than in its later years. So instead of spreading the total cost of the asset over its productive lifespan, it is expensed at a constant rate. The depreciated value of an asset can be found by calculating the value at the end of each year or by using the depreciation formula.

The reducing balance method means to find the value of the asset at the end of **each** year.

Depreciation formula

$$F = P(1 - i)^t$$

Where: F = final value (net book value, NBV)
          P = original value at the start of the period
          i = rate, in decimal form
          t = number of years   (see booklet of formulae and tables, page 30)

key point

The depreciation formula is very similar to the compound interest formula, but the rate is deducted because the value is decreasing rather than increasing.

Example

(i) A motorbike was bought for €15,375 including Value Added Tax (VAT) at 23%. What was the cost price excluding VAT?

(ii) The motorbike depreciates at a rate of 12% per annum on its cost price (excluding VAT). Use the reducing balance method to find the value of the motorbike after three years.

Solution

(i) €15,375 = 123%
         €125 = 1%   (divide by 123)
      €12,500 = 100%   (multiply by 100)
     Therefore, the cost price excluding VAT was €12,500.

(ii) Use the reducing balance method:
     Year 1: $P = 12,500$, $i = 12\% = 0.12$
                    $F = P(1 - i)$
                    $F = 12,500(1 - 0.12)$
                    $F = 12,500(0.88) = 11,000$

Year 2: $P = 11,000$, $i = 12\% = 0.12$

$$F = P(1 - i)$$
$$F = 11,000(1 - 0.12)$$
$$F = 11,000(0.88) = 9,680$$

Year 3: $P = 9,680$, $i = 12\% = 0.12$

$$F = P(1 - i)$$
$$F = 9,680(1 - 0.12)$$
$$F = 9,680(0.88) = 8,518.40$$

Therefore, the value of the motorbike is €8,518·40 after three years.

key point

If the question had not specified using the reducing balance method we could have used the formula:

$$F = P(1 - i)^t$$

where P = €12,500, i = 12%, t = 3.

exam Q

A machine which cost €35,650 depreciates to a value of €480 in 10 years.

(i) Find the annual rate of depreciation.
(ii) Find the net book value (NBV), to the nearest euro, at the end of the sixth year.
(iii) If the company sold the machine at the end of the sixth year for €2,200, calculate the percentage loss they would make on its NBV at that time. Give your answer to the nearest whole number.

Solution

(i) Use the depreciation formula, where $F = 480$, $P = 35,650$, $t = 10$, i = ?

$$F = P(1 - i)^t$$
$$480 = 35,650(1 - i)^{10}$$
$$\frac{480}{35,650} = (1 - i)^{10}$$
$$\sqrt[10]{\frac{480}{35,650}} = 1 - i \qquad \text{(Find 10}^{\text{th}} \text{ root of both sides)}$$
$$0.6500 = 1 - i$$
$$i = 1 - 0.6500$$
$$i = 0.35$$
$$\text{Rate} = 35\%$$

(ii) Use the depreciation formula to find the value of the machine after six years:

$F = ?, P = 35,650, t = 6, i = 0.35$

$$F = P(1 - i)^t$$

$$F = 35,650(1 - 0.35)^6$$

$$F = 35,650(0.65)^6$$

$$F = 2,688.68$$

At the end of the sixth year, the machine is worth €2,689.

(iii) Loss = current value − selling price

$$= €2,688.68 - €2,200$$

$$= €488.68$$

$$\text{Percentage loss} = \frac{\text{Loss}}{\text{Value}} \times 100$$

$$= \frac{488.68}{2,688.68} \times 100$$

$$= 18.2\%$$

Thus, selling the machine for €2,200 would be a loss of 18% of its current NBV.

Income tax

The following is called the income tax equation:

gross tax − tax credit = tax payable

Gross tax is calculated as follows:

| Standard rate on all income up to the standard rate cut-off point | + | A higher rate on all income above the standard rate cut-off point |

Deductions on income

All deductions can be divided into two categories: statutory and non-statutory.

Statutory deductions:	Non-statutory deductions:
Compulsory deductions, which must be paid.	Voluntary deductions, which the worker can choose to pay or not pay.
Examples:	Examples:
Income tax	Pension contributions
Pay-Related Social Insurance (PRSI)	Trade union subscriptions
Universal Social Charge (USC)	Health insurance payments

Pay-Related Social Insurance (PRSI)

PRSI is made up of social insurance and health contributions. The social insurance part goes to funds to pay for social welfare and benefits in Ireland. The health contribution part goes to the Department of Health and Children to help fund health services in Ireland. The amount of PRSI an employee pays depends on how much they earn and is calculated as a percentage of their earnings. The employer will also pay a contribution to the employee's PRSI payment.

Universal Social Charge (USC)

The Universal Social Charge is a tax payable on gross income. This tax was introduced in 2011 to provide additional income for the state. The rates for USC can be changed in the annual budget. At the time of publishing, the rates were as follows:

If a worker earns under €10,036 in total, then they do not pay USC.
If a worker earns over €10,036, USC is charged on all income, as follows:

2%	On the first €10,036
4%	On the next €5,980
7%	On the balance

You are not required to learn off USC rates or PRSI bands. They will be provided in the question, if required.

Example

A woman has a gross yearly income of €48,000. She has a standard rate cut-off point of €27,500 and a tax credit of €3,852. The standard rate of tax is 18% of income up to the standard rate cut-off point and 37% on all income above the standard rate cut-off point.

Calculate:

 (i) The amount of gross tax for the year
 (ii) The amount of tax paid for the year

Solution

 (i) Gross income: €48,000
     Tax is charged as: €27,500 at 18% and €20,500 at 37%

Gross tax = 18% of €27,500 + 37% of €20,500

$$= €27,500 × 0·18 + €20,500 × 0·37$$

$$= €4,950 + €7,585$$

$$= €12,535$$

(ii) Income tax equation:

Gross tax − tax credit = tax payable

€12,535 − €3,852 = €8,683

Therefore, she paid €8,683 in tax.

Example

Kevin has a gross yearly income of €62,500. He has a standard rate cut-off point of €29,000 and a tax credit of €4,650. The standard rate of tax is 22% of income up to the standard rate cut-off point and 41% on all income above the standard rate cut-off point.

Calculate:

(i)   Kevin's gross tax for the year
(ii) The amount of tax paid for the year
(iii) The total USC Kevin must pay (based on the previous table given)
(iv) Kevin's net pay for the year

Solution

(i)   Gross income: €62,500
         Tax: €29,000 at 22% + €33,500 at 41%
         Tax: €6,380 + €13,735
       Gross tax: €20,115

(ii)   Net tax = gross tax − tax credit
        Net tax = €20,115 − €4,650
        Net tax = €15,465

(iii) USC:
      2% on €10,036 = € 200·72
      4% on €5,980 = € 239·20
      7% on €46,484 = €3,253·88
         Total USC = € 3,693·80

USC rates for this question	
2%	On the first €10,036
4%	On the next €5,980
7%	On the balance

(iv) Net pay = gross pay − net tax − USC
     Net pay = €62,500 − €15,465 − €3,693.80
     Net pay = €43,341·20

The table shows the hours Tony worked over five days.

Day	Wednesday	Thursday	Friday	Saturday	Sunday
Hours worked	6	7	7·5	6	h

Tony's basic rate of pay is €13·50 per hour.

He is paid one and a half times the basic rate for work on Saturday and Sunday.

(i) Calculate Tony's total pay for Wednesday, Thursday, Friday and Saturday.

(ii) Tony was paid a total of €540 for the five days' work. Find h, the number of hours Tony worked on Sunday.

(iii) Tony pays income tax at the rate of 20%. He has weekly tax credits of €63. How much income tax does he pay?

(iv) Tony pays the USC at the rate of 2% on the first €193, 4% on the next €115 and 7% on the balance. Calculate the amount of USC Tony pays.

(v) Tony also pays PRSI. His total weekly deductions amount to €76·92. How much PRSI does Tony pay?

Solution

(i) Tony is paid €13·50 per hour for Wednesday, Thursday and Friday.

Tony is paid €13·50 × 1·5 = €20·25 per hour for Saturday and Sunday.

Total pay = (hours on Wed, Thurs and Fri × €13·50) + (hours on Sat × € 20·25)

$$= ((6 + 7 + 7·5) × €13·50) + (6 × €20·25)$$

$$= (20·5 × €13·50) + (6 × €20·25)$$

$$= €276·75 + €121·50$$

$$= €398·25$$

(ii) Total for five days = (total for Wed to Sat) + (total earned on Sunday)

$$€540 = €398·25 + (\text{total earned on Sunday})$$

$$€141·75 = \text{total earned on Sunday}$$

$$€141·75 = (\text{hours worked on Sunday} × €20·25)$$

$$€141·75 = (h × €20·25)$$

$$7 = h \qquad \text{(divide both sides by €20·25)}$$

Therefore, Tony worked for 7 hours on Sunday.

(iii) Gross tax = 20% of gross wages

$$= (0\cdot2) \times €540$$

$$= €108$$

Net tax = gross tax − tax credit

Net tax = €108 − €63

Net tax = €45

(iv) USC based on a gross wage of €540:

2% on €193 = € 3·86

4% on €115 = € 4·60

7% on €232 = €16·24

Total USC = €24·70

(v) Total deductions = tax + USC + PRSI

$$€76\cdot92 = €45 + €24\cdot70 + PRSI$$

$$€76\cdot92 = €69\cdot70 + PRSI$$

$$€76\cdot92 - €69\cdot70 = PRSI$$

$$€7\cdot22 = PRSI$$

The standard rate of income is 20% and the higher rate is 42%.

Cathy has weekly tax credits of €42 and a standard-rate cut-off point of €320.

Until recently, Cathy had a gross weekly income of €850.

(i) Calculate the tax Cathy paid each week.

(ii) After getting a pay rise, Cathy's weekly after-tax income increased by €37·70. Calculate the increase in Cathy's gross weekly income.

Solution

(i)   Gross income: €850

          Tax: €320 at 20% + €530 at 42%

          Tax: €64 + €222·60

     Gross tax: €286·60

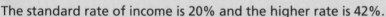

Net tax = gross tax − tax credit

Net tax = €286·60 − €42

Net tax = €244·60

(ii) The income from a pay increase will be taxed at a rate of 42% since Cathy has already exceeded the standard rate cut-off point.

Thus, the after-tax income of €37·70 is 58% of her pay rise (the amount Cathy receives **after** 42% tax has been deducted):

$$€37·70 = 58\%$$
$$€0·65 = 1\% \qquad \text{(divide both sides by 58)}$$
$$€65 = 100\% \qquad \text{(multiply both sides by 100)}$$

Therefore, Cathy received a pay increase of €65 per week.

 aims

- [ ] To revise how to find the slope/gradient of a line
- [ ] To develop the understanding that calculus is simply about rate of change
- [ ] To become familiar with the notation of calculus

Calculus helps us answer questions such as:

- How slanted is a line?
- How steep is a line?
- What is the slope of a line?
- How does the graph of a curve change as it moves across the page?
- How can we measure the rate of change of a curve?

To begin, we consider a very simple example.

Example

Look at the following straight line graphs and write down their slopes.

(i)

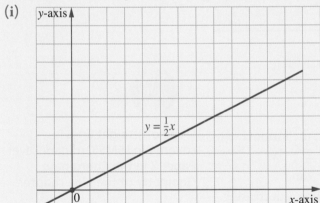

(ii)

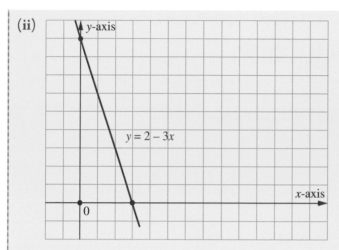

Solution

(i) Use the rule for slope $= \dfrac{\text{Rise}}{\text{Run}}$

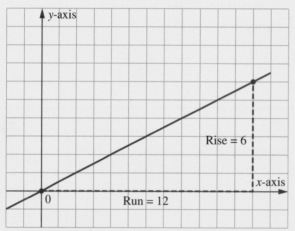

$$\text{Slope} = \frac{6\,\text{units}}{12\,\text{units}} = \frac{1}{2}$$

(ii) From coordinate geometry, the formula
$y = mx + c$ applied to $y = 2 - 3x$
tells us the slope $= m = -3$ and
the minus sign tells us the line is decreasing.

key point

Slope of straight lines is covered in LSMS Ordinary Level Paper 2 in the Coordinate Geometry of the Line chapter.

Alternatively, for part (i) or part (ii) we could use another coordinate geometry formula:

$$m = \text{slope} = \frac{y_2 - y_1}{x_2 - x_1}.$$

Select any two points on the graphs and calculate the slope in the usual way.

Example

Paula cycles her bicycle at a constant speed along a 600 m stretch of road. It takes Paula 120 seconds to complete the stretch.

(i) At what speed did Paula travel along this road?

(ii) The indicated graph shows Paula's journey. Calculate the slope of the graph that represents Paula's journey.

(iii) Can you relate your answer from part (i) to your answer from part (ii)?

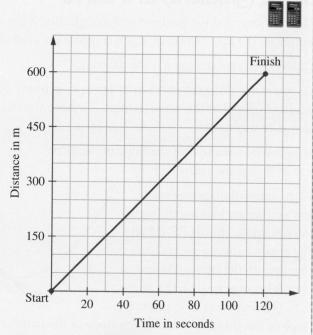

Solution

(i) We use the rule: Speed $= \dfrac{\text{Distance}}{\text{Time}}$

$$\Rightarrow \text{Paula's speed} = \frac{600\,\text{m}}{120\,\text{secs}}$$

$$= 5\text{m/sec}$$

(ii) Reading from the graph: Start $= (0, 0) = (x_1, y_1)$

Finish $= (120, 600) = (x_2, y_2)$

$$\text{Slope} = m = \frac{y_2 - y_1}{x_2 - x_1} = \frac{600 - 0}{120 - 0} = \frac{600}{120} = 5$$

(iii) The answer to part (i) equals the answer to part (ii).

This is not a coincidence. We shall return to this idea in Chapter 15.

It is vital to remember that speed = the rate of change.
This idea is fundamental for success in this exam topic.

Slope (gradient) of a curve

We have seen that the gradient of a straight line is the same at all
points on the line. However, this is not true on a curve.

Consider the curve shown is the diagram.

As you move along the curve from point C to point D, the
gradient (slope) of the curve changes – it becomes steeper,
that is, m increases.

Suppose we want to find the slope of the curve
$y = x^2 + 1$ at the point $P(1, 2)$.

In the series of diagrams below,
it is as if we are looking through a
microscope at chords PS, PR and
PQ drawn between points close
together on the curve. As the
chords become smaller, the points
S, R, Q move closer to P and the
slope of the chord approaches the slope of the tangent at P.

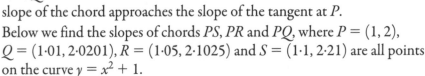

Below we find the slopes of chords PS, PR and PQ, where $P = (1, 2)$,
$Q = (1\cdot01, 2\cdot0201)$, $R = (1\cdot05, 2\cdot1025)$ and $S = (1\cdot1, 2\cdot21)$ are all points
on the curve $y = x^2 + 1$.

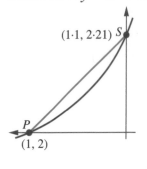

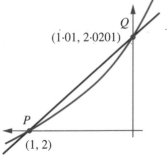

$$\text{Slope } PS = \frac{2\cdot21 - 2}{1\cdot1 - 1}$$

$$= \frac{0\cdot21}{0\cdot1}$$

$$= 2\cdot1$$

$$\text{Slope } PR = \frac{2\cdot1025 - 2}{1\cdot05 - 1}$$

$$= \frac{0\cdot1025}{0\cdot05}$$

$$= 2\cdot05$$

$$\text{Slope } PQ = \frac{2\cdot0201 - 2}{1\cdot01 - 1}$$

$$= \frac{0\cdot0201}{0\cdot01}$$

$$= 2\cdot01$$

This suggests (but does not prove) that the slope of the curve $y = x^2 + 1$ at the point $(1, 2)$ is 2.

We could say 'as the line becomes a tangent to the curve at the point P, its slope becomes 2'.

This idea of points getting closer together is referred to as a limit in mathematics. The process of finding this limiting value is called differentiation. For neatness, this limit is written as $\dfrac{dy}{dx}$ (pronounced 'dee y, dee x') or $f'(x)$ (pronounced 'f dash of x' or 'f prime of x').

$\dfrac{dy}{dx}$ or $f'(x)$ is called the differential coefficient or first derivate of y with respect to x.

The advantage of the notation $\dfrac{dy}{dx}$ is that it tells us which quantities are being compared.

$\dfrac{dy}{dx}$ is the derivative of y with respect to x.

$\dfrac{ds}{dt}$ is the derivative of s with respect to t.

$\dfrac{dA}{dr}$ is the derivative of A with respect to r.

It is worth becoming familiar with the following table:

Rates of change	Independent variable	Dependent variable	In calculus we write as
y-value changes as x-value changes	x	y	$\dfrac{dy}{dx}$
Distance, s, changes as time, t, changes	t	s	$\dfrac{ds}{dt}$
Speed, v, changes as time, t, changes	t	v	$\dfrac{dv}{dt}$
Area, A, changes as radius, r, changes	r	A	$\dfrac{dA}{dr}$
Production costs, p, changes as quality, q, of product changes	q	p	$\dfrac{dp}{dq}$

key point

An independent variable is a variable that is free from outside control, i.e. is not affected by anything else.

A dependent variable is a variable that can be controlled or determined by some other variable or event.

exam
Q

Two cylindrical containers *D*, and *E*, are being filled with water.

The volume of water increases at the same rate in both and the height of both containers is 6 cm.
Container *E* is full after 39 seconds.

The volume of container *E* is three and a quarter times the volume of container *D*.

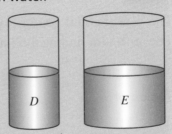

(i) Write down the time it takes for container *D* to fill.

(ii) On the grid below, sketch a graph to show the rate at which the height of the water level changes with time for both containers. Put both containers on the same grid.

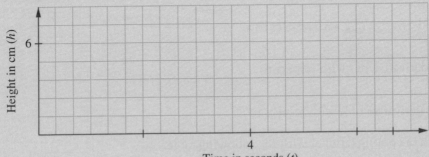

Solution

(i) Since $3\frac{1}{4}$ times the volume of *D* = the volume of *E*

Then the volume of $D = \dfrac{1}{3\frac{1}{4}}$ (the volume of *E*)

$\Rightarrow$ The time taken to fill $D = \dfrac{\text{The time taken to fill } E}{3\frac{1}{4}}$

$= \dfrac{39}{3\frac{1}{4}} = 12$ secs.

(ii)

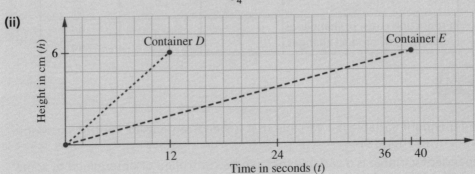

A cylindrical container P, and an inverted cone Q (as shown below) are being filled with water. The height and radius of both containers are equal. The volume of water increases at the same rate in both containers.

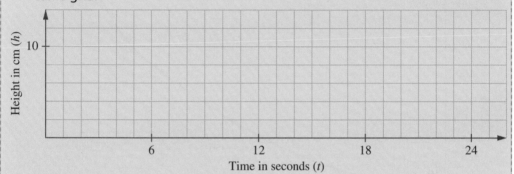

Container P is full after 24 seconds.

(i) Write down the time it takes for container Q to fill. Justify your answer.

(ii) On the grid below, sketch a graph to show the rate at which the height of the water level changes with time for both containers. Put both containers on the same grid.

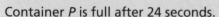

Solution

(i) Volume of cylinder $= \pi r^2 h$ ⎤
Volume of cone $= \dfrac{1}{3}\pi r^2 h$ ⎦ (from booklet of formulae and tables, page 10)

Since the heights and radii are equal, the volume of the cone, Q, is $\frac{1}{3}$ the volume of the cylinder, P.

$\Rightarrow$ It takes $\dfrac{1}{3}$(24 seconds) $= 8$ secs to fill Q.

(ii)

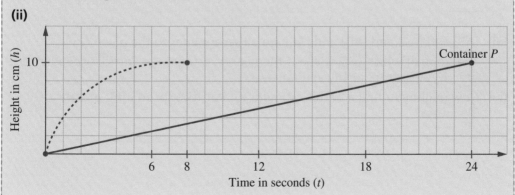

key point

The increase in the height of the water in the inverted cone is particularly rapid in the initial stage. This is due to the pointed vertex of the cone, which causes the height, h, of the water to rise rapidly initially and then progressively slow down.

exam Q

Below is a distance time graph of a 1 kilometre warm-up run by Patrick before he starts a training session.

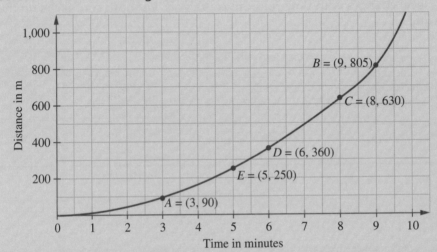

(i)   What was Patrick's average speed for the run in metres/min? Give your answer correct to the nearest metre.

(ii) Complete the following table by using the formula $\dfrac{y_2 - y_1}{x_2 - x_1}$.

Slope of [AB]	Slope of [AC]	Slope of [AD]	Slope of [AE]

(iii) [AB] and [AC] and [AD] and [AE] are all secant lines to the given curve.
      The slope of which secant line is the nearest estimate to Patrick's speed after exactly 3 minutes? Justify your answer.

(iv) How might you find a better estimate for Patrick's speed after exactly 3 minutes?

Solution

(i) Speed $= \dfrac{\text{Distance}}{\text{Time}} = \dfrac{1{,}000}{9 \cdot 7} = 103$ m/sec

(ii) Use $m = \dfrac{y_2 - y_1}{x_2 - x_1}$ four times.

Slope of [AB]	Slope of [AC]	Slope of [AD]	Slope of [AE]
$(3, 90) = (x_1, y_1)$	$(3, 90) = (x_1, y_1)$	$(3, 90) = (x_1, y_1)$	$(3, 90) = (x_1, y_1)$
$(9, 805) = (x_2, y_2)$	$(8, 630) = (x_2, y_2)$	$(6, 360) = (x_2, y_2)$	$(5, 250) = (x_2, y_2)$
$m = \dfrac{805 - 90}{9 - 3}$	$m = \dfrac{630 - 90}{8 - 3}$	$m = \dfrac{360 - 90}{6 - 3}$	$m = \dfrac{250 - 90}{5 - 3}$
$m = \dfrac{715}{6} = 119 \cdot 2$	$m = \dfrac{540}{5} = 108$	$m = \dfrac{270}{3} = 90$	$m = \dfrac{160}{2} = 80$

(iii) The slope of the secant [AE] gives the best estimate.

Consider the secant [AF] where $F = (4, 160)$.

$\Rightarrow m = \dfrac{160 - 90}{4 - 3} = \dfrac{70}{1} = 70$, which is an even better estimate of Patrick's speed after 3 minutes.

(iv) Find the slope of the tangent to the curve at A.

As the secant line becomes the tangent at A, we find Patrick's exact speed after 3 minutes.

13 Differential Calculus II: Differentiation by Rule

aims

- ☐ To learn how to differentiate by rule
- ☐ To be able to evaluate derivatives for specific values
- ☐ To gain the skill to write down the first and second derivative of a function in an instant

Notation summary

Differentiation, or differential calculus, is the branch of mathematics measuring rates of change.

$$y = f(x)$$

$$\frac{dy}{dx} = f'(x)$$

If $y = f(x)$, then $\dfrac{dy}{dx}$ or $f'(x)$ gives the **rate of change of y with respect to x.**

$\dfrac{dy}{dx}$ or $f'(x)$ is called the **differential coeffcient** or **first derivative of y with respect to x.**

Differentiation by rule

It would be very tedious and time consuming if we had to use the concept of limit every time we wanted to find the rate of change/slope of a tangent to a curve. To speed up the process, we learn how to apply the general rule for differentiation.

(see the booklet of formulae and tables, page 25)

The general rule:

If $y = x^n$ then $\dfrac{dy}{dx} = nx^{n-1}$

If $y = ax^n$ then $\dfrac{dy}{dx} = nax^{n-1}$

In words:

Multiply by the power and reduce the power by 1.

Example

Differentiate the following with respect to x.

(i) $y = 7x^2$ (ii) $y = 4x$ (iii) $y = 2x^3$ (iv) $y = 5$

Solution

(i) $y = 7x^2$ $\dfrac{dy}{dx} = 2(7x^{2-1}) = 14x^1 = 14x$

(ii) $y = 4x = 4x^1$ $\dfrac{dy}{dx} = 1(4x^{1-1}) = 4x^0 = 4$

As $x^0 = 1$.

(iii) $y = 2x^3$ $\dfrac{dy}{dx} = 3(2x^{3-1}) = 6x^2$

key point

(iv) $y = 5 = 5x^0$ $\dfrac{dy}{dx} = 0(5x^{0-1}) = 0$

Part (iv) leads to the rule:
The derivative of a
constant is zero.

key point

The line $y = 5$ is a horizontal line. Its slope is 0. Therefore, its derivative (which is also its slope) equals zero.

$y = 5$

Sum or difference

If the expression to be differentiated contains more than one term, simply differentiate each term separately in the expression.

Example

(i) If $y = 4x^3 - x + 3$, find $\dfrac{dy}{dx}$.

(ii) If $f(x) = 10 + x - x^2$, find $f'(x)$.

Solution

(i) $y = 4x^3 - x + 3$

$\dfrac{dy}{dx} = 12x^2 - 1$

(ii) $f(x) = 10 + x - x^2$

$f'(x) = 1 - 2x$

Evaluating derivatives

We may be asked to find the value of the derivative for a particular value of the function.

Example

(i) If $f(x) = 3x^3 - x^2 + x$, find the value of $f'(-2)$.

(ii) If $s = t^3 + 5t^2 - 3t + 7$, find the value of $\dfrac{ds}{dt}$ when $t = 5$.

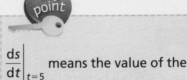

key point

$\left.\dfrac{ds}{dt}\right|_{t=5}$ means the value of the derived function when $t = 5$.

Solution

(i) $f(x) = 3x^3 - x^2 + x$

$f'(x) = 9x^2 - 2x + 1$

$f'(-2) = 9(-2)^2 - 2(-2) + 1$

$f'(-2) = 36 + 4 + 1 = 41$

(ii) $s = t^3 + 5t^2 - 3t + 7$

$\dfrac{ds}{dt} = 3t^2 + 10t - 3$

$\left.\dfrac{ds}{dt}\right|_{t=5} = 3(5)^2 + 10(5) - 3$

$= 75 + 50 - 3 = 122$

The table below shows some values of two functions, $f(x)$ and $g(x)$, and of their derivatives, $f'(x)$ and $g'(x)$.

x	1	2	3	4
$f(x)$	8	7	2	5
$g(x)$	1	-2	2	-6
$f'(x)$	-2	6	0	-4
$g'(x)$	-15	-5	-3	3

From the table above, evaluate the following.

(i) $f(x) + g(x)$ when $x = 4$

(ii) $g(x) - f(x)$ when $x = 2$

(iii) $f'(x) + g'(x)$ when $x = 1$

(iv) $f'(x) - g'(x)$ when $x = 2$

(v) $\dfrac{d}{dx}(f(x) + g(x))$ when $x = 3$

Solution

Reading from the table below, we find:

x	1	2	3	4
$f(x)$	8	7	2	5
$g(x)$	1	-2	2	-6
$f'(x)$	-2	6	0	-4
$g'(x)$	-15	-5	-3	3

(i) $f(x) + g(x) = f(4) + g(4) = 5 - 6 = -1$ (Red circles)

(ii) $g(x) - f(x) = g(2) - f(2) = -2 - 7 = -9$ (Green circles)

(iii) $f'(x) + g'(x) = f'(1) + g'(1) = -2 - 15 = -17$ (Red diamonds)

(iv) $f'(x) - g'(x) = f'(2) - g'(2) = 6 - (-5) = 6 + 5 = 11$ (Green diamonds)

(v) $\dfrac{d}{dx}(f(x) + g(x)) = f'(x) + g'(x)$

$$= f'(3) + g'(3) = 0 - 3 = -3$$

Second derivatives

The derivative of $\dfrac{dy}{dx}$, that is, $\dfrac{d}{dx}\left(\dfrac{dy}{dx}\right)$, is denoted by $\dfrac{d^2y}{dx^2}$ and is called the **second derivative of y with respect to x.**

$\dfrac{d^2y}{dx^2}$ is pronounced 'dee two y, dee x squared'.

The derivative of $f'(x)$ is denoted by $f''(x)$ and is called the **second derivative of $f(x)$ with respect to x.**

Example

(i) If $y = 10 + x - 2x^2$, find $\dfrac{d^2y}{dx^2}$.

(ii) If $f(x) = 4x^3 - 5x$, find $f''(x)$.

Solution

(i) $y = 10 + x - 2x^2$

$\dfrac{dy}{dx} = 1 - 4x$

(differentiate again)

$\dfrac{d^2y}{dx^2} = -4$

(ii) $f(x) = 4x^3 - 5x$

$f'(x) = 12x^2 - 5$

(differentiate again)

$f''(x) = 24x$

---

key point

$f''(x)$ and $\dfrac{d^2y}{dx^2}$ both represent the second derivative.

Example

(i) If $f(t) = 1 + t - t^2 - t^3$, find $f''(t)$ and $f''(-3)$.

(ii) If $A = 15 - 3x + 2x^2$, find $\dfrac{d^2A}{dx^2}$ when $x = 5$.

Solution

(i) $f(t) = 1 + t - t^2 - t^3$

$f'(t) = 1 - 2t - 3t^2$

$f''(t) = -2 - 6t$

$f''(-3) = -2 - 6(-3)$

$= -2 + 18$

$= 16$

(ii) $A = 15 - 3x + 2x^2$

$\dfrac{dA}{dx} = -3 + 4x$

$\dfrac{d^2A}{dx^2} = 4$

$\left. \dfrac{d^2A}{dx^2} \right|_{x=5} = 4$

key point

In (ii) $\dfrac{d^2A}{dx^2} = 4$, a constant.

exam Q

(i) If $A = \pi r^2$, show that $A + \dfrac{3}{2}\left(\dfrac{dA}{dr}\right) + \dfrac{d^2A}{dr^2} = \pi(r + 2)(r + 1)$.

(ii) If $V = \dfrac{4}{3}\pi r^3$, show that $V\left(\dfrac{d^2V}{dr^2}\right) - \dfrac{2}{3}\left(\dfrac{dV}{dr}\right)^2 = 0$.

Solution

(i) $A = \pi r^2$

$\dfrac{dA}{dr} = 2\pi r$

$\dfrac{d^2A}{dr^2} = 2\pi$

$A + \dfrac{3}{2}\left(\dfrac{dA}{dr}\right) + \dfrac{d^2A}{dr^2}$

$= \pi r^2 + \dfrac{3}{2}(2\pi r) + 2\pi$

$= \pi(r^2 + 3r + 2)$

$= \pi(r + 2)(r + 1)$

(ii) $V = \dfrac{4}{3}\pi r^3$

$\dfrac{dV}{dr} = 4\pi r^2$

$\dfrac{d^2V}{dr^2} = 8\pi r$

$V\dfrac{d^2V}{dr^2} - \dfrac{2}{3}\left(\dfrac{dV}{dr}\right)^2$

$= \left(\dfrac{4}{3}\pi r^3\right)(8\pi r) - \dfrac{2}{3}(4\pi r^2)^2$

$= \dfrac{32}{3}\pi^2 r^4 - \dfrac{2}{3}16\pi^2 r^4$

$= \dfrac{32}{3}\pi^2 r^4 - \dfrac{32}{3}\pi^2 r^4 = 0$

key point

$r^2 + 3r + 2 = (r + 2)(r + 1) \Rightarrow$ factorisation from algebra is a vital skill to complete this calculus question.

key point

$\dfrac{d^2V}{dr^2} \neq \left(\dfrac{dV}{dr}\right)^2$

14 Differential Calculus III: Applications to Curves and Curve Sketching

□ To understand the importance of slope of a tangent to a curve and how to find it

□ To be able to find the equation of a tangent to a curve given a point on the curve

□ Know how to find the coordinates of turning points on a curve

□ To understand the importance of the skills you learned in algebra and to revise them if necessary

□ To the necessary insights into decreasing and increasing sections of curves and what this means for $\dfrac{dy}{dx}$

□ To acquire the skill to sketch individual curves and families of curves

In this chapter we study the link between calculus and curves.

Equation of a tangent

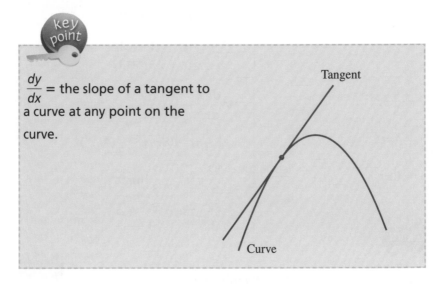

key point

$\dfrac{dy}{dx}$ = the slope of a tangent to a curve at any point on the curve.

Tangent

Curve

To find the slope and equation of a tangent to a curve at a given point (x_1, y_1) on the curve, do the following.

Step 1: Find $\dfrac{dy}{dx}$.

Step 2: Evaluate $\dfrac{dy}{dx}\bigg|_{x=x_1}$ (this gives the slope of the tangent, m)

Step 3: Use m (from step 2) and the given point (x_1, y_1) in the equation:

$(y - y_1) = m(x - x_1)$ (from the booklet of formulae and tables, page 18)

- Sometimes only the value of x is given. When this happens, substitute the value of x into the original function to find y for step 3.
- Huge link here between calculus and coordinate geometry.

Find the equation of the tangent to the curve $y = x^3 - x^2 - 5x - 6$ at the point $(2, -12)$.

Solution

Step 1: $y = x^3 - x^2 - 5x - 6$

$\dfrac{dy}{dx} = 3x^2 - 2x - 5$

Step 2: Evaluate $\dfrac{dy}{dx}$ at $x = 2$.

$\dfrac{dy}{dx} = 3x^2 - 2x - 5$

$\dfrac{dy}{dx}\bigg|_{x=2} = 3(2)^2 - 2(2) - 5 = 12 - 4 - 5 = 3$

Step 3: Use $y - y_1 = m(x - x_1)$

where $m = \dfrac{dy}{dx} = 3$ and $(x_1, y_1) = (2, -12)$

$\Rightarrow \quad y - (-12) = 3(x - 2)$

$y + 12 = 3x - 6$

$y = 3x - 18$ is the equation.

Sometimes the value of $\dfrac{dy}{dx}$ (slope of the curve at any point on it) is given and we need to find the coordinates of the point, or points, corresponding to this slope.

When this happens, do the following.

Step 1: Find $\dfrac{dy}{dx}$.

Step 2: Let $\dfrac{dy}{dx}$ equal the given value of the slope and solve this equation for x.

Step 3: Substitute the x values obtained in step 2 into the original function to get the corresponding values of y.

Example

Find the point on the curve $y = x^2 + 12x + 6$ at which the slope is 2.

Solution

$$y = x^2 + 12x + 6 \implies \frac{dy}{dx} = 2x + 12$$

$$\text{Slope} = \frac{dy}{dx} = 2$$

We have an equation in disguise. By comparision

$$\implies \quad 2x + 12 = 2$$
$$2x = 2 - 12$$
$$2x = -10$$
$$x = -5$$

key point

The question asks for the point on the curve. This requires an x **and** a y component in our answer.

Put $x = -5$ into

$y = x^2 + 12x + 6$ to get

$y = (-5)^2 + 12(-5) + 6 = 25 - 60 + 6 = -29$.

$\therefore$ The point on the curve is $(-5, -29)$.

Let $y = x^2 - 5x + 6$, $x \in \mathbb{R}$.

Find the slopes of the tangents to the graph of y at the points $(2, 0)$ and $(3, 0)$ and investigate if these two tangents are at right angles to each other.

Solution

$$y = x^2 - 5x + 6$$

$$\frac{dy}{dx} = 2x - 5 \quad \text{(slope at any point)}$$

at $(2, 0)$, $x = 2$	at $(3, 0)$, $x = 3$
$\left.\dfrac{dy}{dx}\right\|_{x=2} = 2(2) - 5$	$\left.\dfrac{dy}{dx}\right\|_{x=3} = 2(3) - 5$
$= 4 - 5$	$= 6 - 5$
$= -1$	$= 1$
$\therefore$ Slope at $x = 2$ is -1	$\therefore$ Slope at $x = 3$ is 1

(Slope at $x = 2$) (Slope at $x = 3$) $= (-1)(1) = -1$
$\therefore$ The tangents are at right angles to each other.

The previous question links the rule for a pair of perpendicular lines $m_1 m_2 = -1$ with the calculus idea on slopes of a tangent.

Let $f(x) = 2x^3 - 3x^2 - 13x + 2, \quad x \in \mathbb{R}$.

(i) Find the derivative of $f(x)$.

(ii) Find the coordinates of the points on the curve $f(x)$ at which the tangents to the curve are parallel to the line $y = 5 - x$.

Solution

(i) For the graph, $y = f(x)$.

Curve: $y = 2x^3 - 3x^2 - 13x + 2$

$$\frac{dy}{dx} = 6x^2 - 6x - 13$$

(ii) Line: $y = 5 - x$

slope $= \dfrac{dy}{dx} = -1$

Given: Slope of curve = Slope of line

$$6x^2 - 6x - 13 = -1$$
$$6x^2 - 6x - 12 = 0$$
$$x^2 - x - 2 = 0$$
$$(x - 2)(x + 1) = 0$$
$$x - 2 = 0 \quad \text{or} \quad x + 1 = 0$$
$$x = 2 \quad \text{or} \quad x = -1$$

key point

If you cannot factorise, then you may use the formula

$$x = \frac{-b \pm \sqrt{b^2 - 4ac}}{2a}$$ to solve for x.

We have the x coordinates on the curve, now we need the y coordinates.

$$y = 2x^3 - 3x^2 - 13x + 2$$

$x = 2$	$x = -1$
$y = 2(2)^3 - 3(2)^2 - 13(2) + 2$	$y = 2(-1)^3 - 3(-1)^2 - 13(-1) + 2$
$\quad = 2(8) - 3(4) - 13(2) + 2$	$\quad = 2(-1) - 3(1) - 13(-1) + 2$
$\quad = 16 - 12 - 26 + 2$	$\quad = -2 - 3 + 13 + 2$
$\quad = 18 - 38$	$\quad = 15 - 5$
$\quad = -20$	$\quad = 10$
$\therefore x = 2, y = -20$	$\therefore x = -1, y = 10$

Thus, $(2, -20)$ and $(-1, 10)$ are the required points.

Maximum and minimum points

A point on a curve at which the slope (gradient) is zero, where $\dfrac{dy}{dx} = 0$, is called a stationary or turning point.

At a stationary point, the tangent to the curve is horizontal (parallel to the x-axis) and we say the curve is flat.

We consider two types of stationary points:

1. Minimum points   2. Maximum points

$\dfrac{dy}{dx}$ can be used to find the local maximum or local minimum points on a curve.

On the right is part of the graph of a cubic function. At the turning points, A and B, the tangents to the curve are horizontal (parallel to the x-axis). In other words, at these points the slope of the tangent is zero. These turning points are also called the **local maximum point**, point A, and the **local minimum point**, point B.

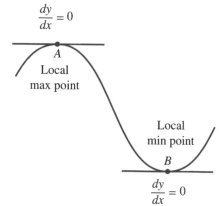

> At a maximum or minimum point, $\dfrac{dy}{dx} = 0$.

To find the maximum or minimum points on a curve, do the following.

Step 1. Find $\dfrac{dy}{dx}$.

Step 2. Let $\dfrac{dy}{dx} = 0$ and solve this equation for x.

Step 3. Substitute the x values obtained in step 2 into the original function to get the corresponding values of y.

Step 4.

Method 1: By comparing the y values we can determine which point is the local maximum or minimum point. The point with the greater y value is the local maximum point and the point with the lower y value is the local minimum point.

Method 2: Find $\dfrac{d^2y}{dx^2}$.

Substitute the x values obtained in step 2 into $\dfrac{d^2y}{dx^2}$.

If $\dfrac{d^2y}{dx^2} > 0$, then it is the minimum point.

If $\dfrac{d^2y}{dx^2} < 0$, then it is the maximum point.

Note: The graph of a quadratic function $f(x) = ax^2 + bx + c$ has only one turning point.

1. If $a > 0$, the turning point will be a minimum.
2. If $a < 0$, the turning point will be a maximum.

Example

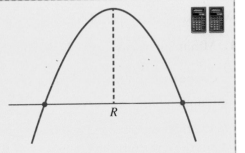

Part of the graph of $y = f(x) = 14x - 5x^2$ is shown.

The x-coordinate of the local maximum point is R. Calculate the value of R.

Solution

$$f(x) = 14x - 5x^2$$
$$f'(x) = 14 - 10x$$
$$f'(x) = 0 \text{ at the local maximum}$$

By comparison
$$14 - 10x = 0$$
$$-10x = -14$$
$$10x = 14$$
$$x = 1.4 \qquad \text{Answer } R = 1.4.$$

Find the local maximum and local minimum points of the curve $f(x) = x^3 - 3x + 2$.

Solution

$$f(x) = x^3 - 3x + 2$$
$$\therefore f'(x) = 3x^2 - 3$$

We know $f'(x) = 0$ at maximum and minimum points

$$\Rightarrow \qquad 3x^2 - 3 = 0$$
$$3(x^2 - 1) = 0 \quad \text{(factorising)}$$
$$3(x - 1)(x + 1) = 0$$

Hence, either $x - 1 = 0$ [or] $x + 1 = 0$

$$x = 1 \quad \text{[or]} \quad x = -1$$

when $x = 1$	when $x = -1$
$f(x) = x^3 - 3x + 2$	$f(-1) = x^3 - 3x + 2$
becomes $f(1) = (1)^3 - 3(1) + 2$	becomes $f(-1) = (-1)^3 - 3(-1) + 2$
$f(1) = 1 - 3 + 2 = 0$	$f(-1) = -1 + 3 + 2 = 4$
$\therefore (1, 0)$ is a turning point.	$\therefore (-1, 4)$ is a turning point.

Which is the maximum point and which is the minimum point?

Method 1: Plot both points on a graph.

By inspection we observe that the maximum is associated with the higher point $\Rightarrow$ maximum $(-1, 4)$.

The minimum is associated with the lower point i.e. minimum $(1, 0)$.

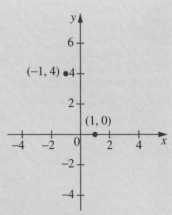

Method 2: $f'(x) = 3x^2 - 3 \quad \Rightarrow \quad f''(x) = 6x$

When $x = 1$

put $x = 1$ into $f''(x) = 6x$

to get $f''(1) = 6(1) = 6$

since $f''(1) = 6 > 0$

we know $x = 1$ gives a minimum

$\Rightarrow \quad (1, 0)$ a local minimum.

When $x = -1$

put $x = -1$ into $f''(x) = 6x$

to get $f''(-1) = 6(-1) = -6$

since $f''(-1) = -6 < 0$

we know $x = -1$ gives a maximum

$\Rightarrow \quad (-1, 4)$ a local maximum.

If $\dfrac{d^2y}{dx^2} > 0 \Rightarrow$ minimum point

If $\dfrac{d^2y}{dx^2} < 0 \Rightarrow$ maximum point

It is possible to draw a rough sketch of $f(x)$ using only the local maximum and local minimum points.

Plot $(-1, 4)$ and $(1, 0)$ as indicated.

Then sketch the graph around those turning points of $f(x)$.

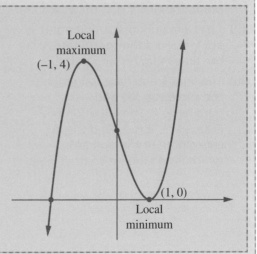

Let $y = 3x^3 - 12x^2 - ax + 3$ for all $x \in \mathbb{R}$ and for $a \in \mathbb{R}$.

y has a turning point (a local minimum or local maximum) at $x = 3$.

Find the value of a.

Solution

$$y = 3x^3 - 12x^2 - ax + 3$$

$$\frac{dy}{dx} = 9x^2 - 24x - a$$

$$\frac{dy}{dx} = 0 \qquad \text{at local minimum/maximum}$$

By comparison: $9x^2 - 24x - a = 0$ at $x = 3$

$$9(3)^2 - 24(3) - a = 0$$
$$81 - 72 - a = 0$$
$$9 - a = 0$$
$$\therefore 9 = a$$

The diagram shows the graph of the cubic function f, defined for $x \in \mathbb{R}$ as

$$f : x \mapsto x^3 - x^2 - x + 6.$$

(i) Find the coordinates of the point at which f cuts the y-axis.

(ii) f has a minimum turning point at $(1, 5)$. Find the coordinates of the maximum turning point.

(iii) The lines k and l are tangents to the curve $y = f(x)$ and l is parallel to k. The equation of k is $4x - y + 9 = 0$. Find the x coordinate of the point at which l is a tangent to the curve.

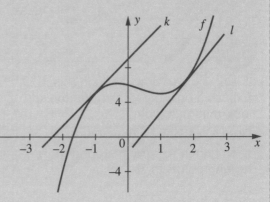

Solution

(i) On the y-axis means $x = 0$

$\Rightarrow f(x) = x^3 - x^2 - x + 6$ becomes

$f(0) = 0 - 0 - 0 + 6 = +6$

Hence, (0, 6) are the coordinates of the required point at which f cuts the y-axis.

(ii) $f(x) = x^3 - x^2 - x + 6$

$f'(x) = 3x^2 - 2x - 1$

$f'(x) = 0$ (at turning points)

$\Rightarrow 3x^2 - 2x - 1 = 0$

$(3x + 1)(x - 1) = 0$ (factorising)

Hence, $3x + 1 = 0$ $\boxed{or}$ $x - 1 = 0$

$3x = -1$ $\boxed{or}$ $x = 1$

$x = -\dfrac{1}{3}$ $\boxed{or}$ $x = 1$

We are given (1, 5) is the minimum turning point.

We conclude $x = -\dfrac{1}{3}$ is associated with the maximum turning point.

$$f(x) = x^3 - x^2 - x + 6$$

$$\Rightarrow f\left(-\frac{1}{3}\right) = \left(-\frac{1}{3}\right)^3 - \left(-\frac{1}{3}\right)^2 - \left(-\frac{1}{3}\right) + 6$$

$$f\left(-\frac{1}{3}\right) = -\frac{1}{27} - \frac{1}{9} + \frac{1}{3} + 6 = 6\frac{5}{27}$$

$\therefore$ Coordinates of maximum turning point $= \left(-\dfrac{1}{3}, 6\dfrac{5}{27}\right)$.

(iii) k has equation $4x - y + 9 = 0$

$-y = -4x - 9$

$y = 4x + 9$

Hence, slope $= \dfrac{dy}{dx} = 4$.

Since l is parallel to k, we know from coordinate geometry of the line that their slopes are equal.

$$\therefore \text{Slope of } l = m = \frac{dy}{dx} = 4$$

From part **(ii)** we had $f'(x) = \dfrac{dy}{dx} = 3x^2 - 2x - 1$.

By comparison we can write $3x^2 - 2x - 1 = 4$

$\Rightarrow 3x^2 - 2x - 5 = 0$

$(3x - 5)(x + 1) = 0$ (factorising)

Hence, $3x - 5 = 0$ ⬚or⬚ $x + 1 = 0$

$\qquad\quad 3x = 5$ ⬚or⬚ $\qquad x = -1$

$\qquad\quad\; x = \dfrac{5}{3}$ ⬚or⬚ $\qquad x = -1$

By observation from the graph, $x = \dfrac{5}{3}$ is the value on the tangent l and on the curve f.

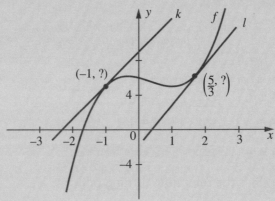

It is worth noting that in a recent exam this question was worth a total of 25 marks, awarded as follows:

Part (i) 10 marks for the correct solution, with 6 marks for any **one** correct step, e.g. $x = 0$.

Part (ii) 10 marks for the correct solution, with 6 marks for any **one** correct step, e.g. $f'(x) = 0$ or $f'(x) = 3x^2 - 2x - 1$.

Part (iii) 5 marks for the correct solution, with 3 marks for any **one** correct step, e.g. slope = 4.

Bear in mind that longer more challenging parts may be awarded less marks than a shorter simpler part.

1. Keep moving through the questions.

2. Attempt every part of every question by **writing something down**.

3. Manage your time budget properly.

It is important to remember that marking schemes vary in consistency from year to year and question to question.

Increasing and decreasing

$\dfrac{dy}{dx}$, being the slope of a tangent to a curve at any point on the curve, can be used to determine if, and where, a curve is increasing or decreasing.

Note: Graphs are read from left to right.

Where a curve is increasing, the tangent to the curve will have a positive slope. Therefore, where a curve is increasing, $\dfrac{dy}{dx}$ will be positive.

Where a curve is decreasing, the tangent to the curve will have a negative slope. Therefore, where a curve is decreasing, $\dfrac{dy}{dx}$ will be negative.

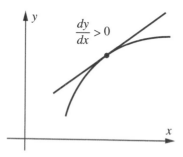

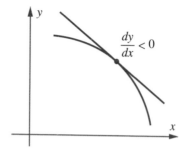

Example

If $f(x) = 7 - 2x - x^3$, show that $f'(x) < 0$ for all $x \in \mathbb{R}$.

Solution

$f(x) = 7 - 2x - x^3$ $\qquad \therefore \qquad f'(x) = -2 - 3x^2$

key point

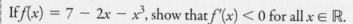

x^2 is always greater than or equal to zero for all $x \in \mathbb{R}$.

We know $-3x^2$ is always less than or equal to zero for all $x \in \mathbb{R}$.
Hence, $-2 - 3x^2$ is always less than zero.
From the key point we conclude that

if $f'(x) = -2 - 3x^2$ then $f'(x)$ is always negative for all $x \in \mathbb{R}$

$\Rightarrow \qquad f'(x) < 0 \quad$ for all $x \in \mathbb{R}$

exam focus

- The fact that (any real number)^2 will always be greater than or equal to zero is worth remembering. This can be a major step towards a successful solution in many tricky exam questions.
- Another major topic link here, this time between functions, graphs and calculus.

exam Q

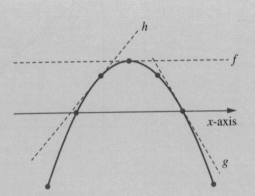

The diagram shows three tangents, *f*, *g* and *h*, to a section of a graph.

(i) Which tangent has a negative slope? Explain your answer.

(ii) Describe the slopes of each of the other two tangents.

Solution

(i) A tangent with a negative slope means the graph is decreasing.

∴ *g* is the tangent with a negative slope.

(ii) The tangent *f* is parallel to the *x*-axis. The tangent *f* makes no angle with the *x*-axis and has slope zero.

h has a positive slope, which is associated with an increasing graph.

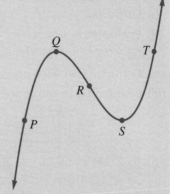

The letters P to T are placed at particular points on the curve $y = f(x)$, as in the diagram.

(i) Which of the points is a local maximum?

(ii) Which of the points is a local minimum?

(iii) What is the slope of the curve $y = f(x)$ at the point marked S?

(iv) At which point is the slope of the curve negative?

(v) In passing from point S to point T and beyond, is $\dfrac{dy}{dx} > 0$ or is $\dfrac{dy}{dx} < 0$? Justify your answer.

Solution

(i) Q is a local maximum.

(ii) S is a local minimum.

(iii) The slope of the curve at S is zero. We say $\dfrac{dy}{dx} = 0$ at the point S or the slope of the tangent at S is zero.

(iv) The slope of the curve is negative at R. (Curve is decreasing at R.)

(v) In passing from S to T and beyond, $\dfrac{dy}{dx} > 0$ because the curve is increasing in that section.

Sketching graphs and their derivatives

For this next section you are required to be very familiar with a previous chapter on quadratic and cubic equations.

In addition, it is vital to know the following:

1. At the turning points of any curve, $f(x)$, its derivative $f'(x) = 0$.
2. Similarly, at the turning points of $f'(x)$, its derivative $f''(x) = 0$.
3. When a function or its derivative is of the form $y = mx + c$, the graph has no turning points and is a straight line.
4. If a function or its derivative is of the form $h(x) = k$, where $k \in R$, the graph of $h(x)$ is a straight line parallel to the x-axis.

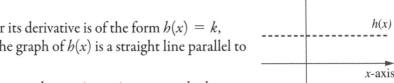

5. In the sections near the turning points, we apply the following:

   (i) For an increasing section of a curve, $f(x)$, we know $f'(x) > 0$, that is, $f'(x)$ is above the x-axis.

   (ii) For a decreasing section of a curve, $f(x)$, we know $f'(x) < 0$, that is, $f'(x)$ is below the x-axis.

$f(x) = 14x - 5x^2$ is a formula that models the path travelled by a ball thrown vertically upwards from the thrower's hand after a time of x seconds.

(i) Find $f'(x)$.

(ii) Evaluate:

    (a) $f'(0)$ (b) $f'(1.4)$ (c) $f'(2.8)$

Comment on each answer and explain the significance of each.

(iii) Graph $f'(x)$ in the space provided

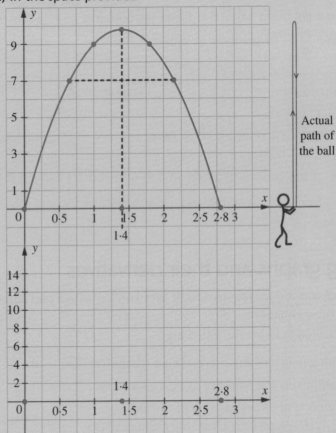

Actual path of the ball

Solution

(i) $f(x) = 14x - 5x^2$

    $f'(x) = 14 - 10x$

(ii) (a) $f'(0) = 14 - 10(0) = 14 - 0 = 14$

    This means 14 m/sec is the speed of the ball as it leaves the throwers hand.

    (b) $f'(1.4) = 14 - 10(1.4) = 14 - 14 = 0$

    This means 0 is the speed of the ball at the maximum height, where the ball changes direction.

(c) $f'(2 \cdot 8) = 14 - 10(2 \cdot 8) = 14 - 28 = -14$

This means -14 m/sec is the speed of the ball as it returns to the throwers hand. The speed is negative as the ball is going down.

The curve $f(x) = 14x - 5x^2$ is symmetric (divides into two equal sections) about the maximum point, i.e. the time $x = 1 \cdot 4$ *secs* is the midpoint of the journey.

(iii) From part **(ii)** we have three points: **(a)** $\Rightarrow (0, 14)$ **(b)** $\Rightarrow (1 \cdot 4, 0)$ **(c)** $\Rightarrow (0, -14)$

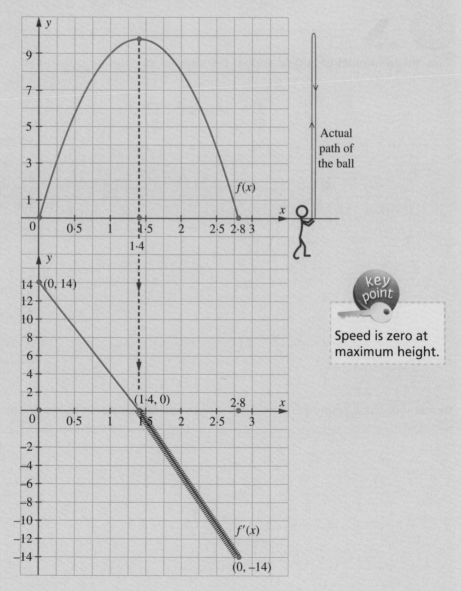

Actual path of the ball

Speed is zero at maximum height.

key point

$f'(x) = 14 - 10x$ is of the form $y = mx + c$. That is to say, it is in the shape of a straight line. This means we only require two points to draw $f'(x)$.

The shaded ▦▦▦ half of $f'(x)$ in the graph is below the x-axis. This corresponds to a decreasing $f(x)$, that is, a negative (downward) speed at all stages on the second half of the journey.

exam focus

Two linked families of curves appear throughout calculus on our course.

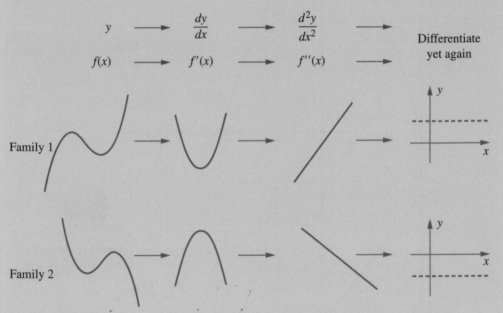

Remember these related curves. They will consistently appear in the exam.

Example

Sketch the graphs of the first and second derivatives of the functions (i) $k(x)$ (ii) $g(x)$ given below.

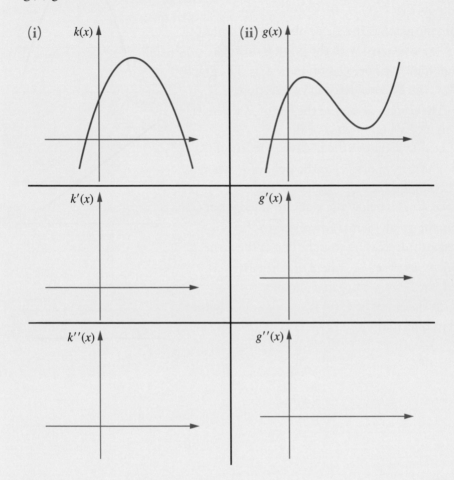

Justify your sketch in each case.

Solution

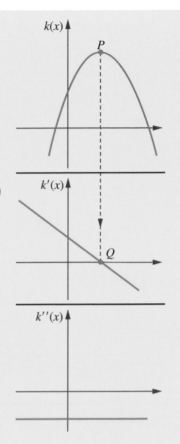

(i) $k(x) \rightarrow k'(x) \rightarrow k''(x)$

At P, the local maximum (turning) point of $k(x)$, we know that $k'(x) = 0$.

From the graph (across), we observe the point Q on $k'(x)$ associated with the point P on $k(x)$.

In addition, we note Q is on the x-axis. The graph of $k(x)$ can be considered in two sections:

(a) The section of $k(x)$ to the left of P, where $k(x)$ is increasing $\Rightarrow k'(x) > 0$, i.e. $k'(x)$ is above the x-axis to the left of Q.

(b) The section of $k(x)$ to the right of P, where $k(x)$ is decreasing $\Rightarrow k'(x) < 0$, i.e. $k'(x)$ is below the x-axis to the right of Q.

From the graph (across) we observe $k'(x)$ is a constantly decreasing straight line of the form

$k'(x) = mx + c$ where m is negative
$\Rightarrow k''(x) = m$ a negative number.

Hence, the graph of $k''(x)$ is a straight line **below** and parallel to the x-axis.

(ii) $g(x) \rightarrow g'(x) \rightarrow g''(x)$

At A and C, the turning points of $g(x)$, we know that $g'(x) = 0$.

From the graph (across), we observe the points B and D on $g'(x)$ associated with the points A and C, respectively, on $g(x)$.

In addition, we note B and D are on the x-axis. The graph of $g(x)$ can be considered in three sections.

(a) The section of $g(x)$ to the left of A where $g(x)$ is increasing $\Rightarrow g'(x) > 0$

i.e. $g'(x)$ is above the x-axis to the left of B.

(b) The section of $g(x)$ between the points A and C, where $g(x)$ is decreasing $\Rightarrow g'(x) < 0$,

i.e. $g'(x)$ is below the x-axis between B and D.

(c) The section of $g(x)$ to the right of C, where $g(x)$ increasing $\Rightarrow g'(x) > 0$,

i.e. $g'(x)$ is above the x-axis to the right of D.

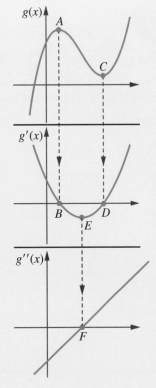

From the graph we observe $g'(x)$ is a U-shaped, quadratic graph with a local minimum (turning) point at E where we know $g''(x) = 0$.

Again from the graph we observe that the point F on $g''(x)$ is associated with the point E on $g'(x)$.

We further observe that F is on the x-axis.

In a similar argument to solution **(i)** we conclude that $g''(x)$ is below the x-axis to the left of F and $g''(x)$ is above the x-axis to the right of F.

$\Rightarrow g''(x)$ is a straight line with a positive slope (as the line is going upwards).

The graph of a cubic function *f* is shown on the right.

One of the four diagrams **A, B, C, D** below shows the graph of the derivative of *f*.

State which one it is. Justify your answer.

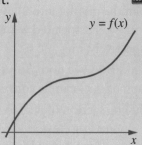
$y = f(x)$

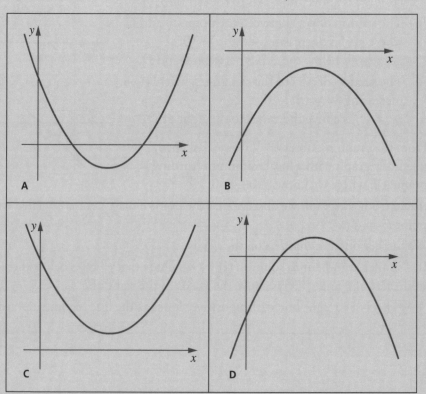

Solution

Answer: C is the graph of $f'(x)$

key point

Justification: By observation $f(x)$ is always increasing

$\Rightarrow f'(x)$ is always positive

$\Rightarrow f'(x)$ is always above the *x*-axis

The graphs of **A, B** and **D** have negative *y* values, indicating decreasing sections in the original $f(x)$, hence they are rejected.

15 Differential Calculus IV: Applications to In-context Problems

aims

☐ To learn about rates of change and how they are applied to in-context questions

☐ To be familiar with what the letters s, v and a represent and how they are linked to each other by calculus

☐ To see how the first and second derivatives can solve questions from such diverse activities as construction, farming, business and finance

Rates of change

The slope (gradient) of a curve is given by

$$\frac{dy}{dx} = \frac{\text{difference in } y}{\text{difference in } x}$$

Hence, the derivative $\dfrac{dy}{dx}$ represents the rate of change of y with respect to x.

It shows how changes in y are related to changes in x.

A common rate of change connects velocity (speed), displacement (distance) and time.

Usually we let s = displacement (distance)

v = velocity (speed)

t = time.

We then write the velocity v at time t is given by

$$v = \frac{ds}{dt}.$$

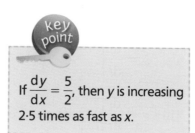

key point

If $\dfrac{dy}{dx} = \dfrac{5}{2}$, then y is increasing 2·5 times as fast as x.

Suppose A and B are any two points on the graph as shown. The length BC represents the distance travelled between the two points A and B.

The length AC represents the time taken to travel this distance.

The gradient (slope) of the line AB represents the average velocity of the body during this time interval.

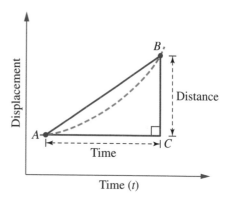

We saw in Chapter 12 [in the technique applied to the curve $y = x^2 + 1$ at the point $(1, 2)$] that as the points get closer together, the gradient of the line gets closer to the gradient of the tangent.

Hence, as B moves closer to A along the indicated curve, the slope of the line AB gets closer to the slope of the tangent at A.

Therefore, the slope of the tangent at A is equal to the velocity at the point A.

Example

The distance s of a body at a time t seconds is given in metres by $s = t^3 - 9t^2 + 27t - 9$. Find:

(i) The velocity of the body at time t
(ii) The initial velocity of the body
(iii) The velocity of the body after 4 seconds

Solution

(i)
$$s = t^3 - 9t^2 + 27t - 9$$

The velocity v is given by $\dfrac{ds}{dt} = 3t^2 - 18t + 27$.

(ii) The initial velocity is the velocity when $t = 0$. Substituting $t = 0$ gives

$$v = \left.\frac{ds}{dt}\right|_{t=0} = 3(0)^2 - 18(0) + 27 = 27\,\text{ms}^{-1}$$

(iii) $v = \left.\dfrac{ds}{dt}\right|_{t=4}$ after 4 seconds

$$v = 3(4)^2 - 18(4) + 27 = 48 - 72 + 27 = 3\,\text{ms}^{-1}$$

key point

When distance is in metres (m) and time in seconds (s), the units of velocity are metres per second, ms^{-1} or m/sec.

Similarly, the rate of change of velocity with respect to time is called the acceleration. The acceleration a at time t is given by:

$$a = \frac{dv}{dt} = \frac{d^2s}{dt^2}$$

A car begins to slow down at P in order to stop at a red traffic light at Q.

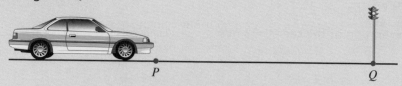

The distance of the car from P, after t seconds, is given by $s = 12t - \frac{3}{2}t^2$, when s is in metres.

  (i) Find the speed of the car as it passes P.
 (ii) Find the time taken to stop.
(iii) The car stops exactly at Q. Find the distance from P to Q.
(iv) Find the acceleration of the car.

Solution

(i) Find the speed of the car as it passes P.

$$s = 12t - \frac{3}{2}t^2$$

$$\text{Speed} = \frac{ds}{dt} = 12 - 2\left(\frac{3}{2}\right)t$$

$$= 12 - 3t \quad \text{(speed at time } t)$$

At $P, t = 0$ (clock is set)

$\text{Speed} = 12 - 3t$

When $t = 0$,

$\text{Speed} = 12 - 3(0) = 12$

$\therefore$ Speed at $P = 12$ m/s.

(ii) Find the time taken to stop.
The car is stopped when its speed $= 0$.

$$\therefore \quad \frac{ds}{dt} = 0$$

$$\therefore \quad 12 - 3t = 0$$

$$-3t = -12$$

$$3t = 12$$

$$t = 4$$

$\therefore$ The car reaches Q after 4 seconds (time taken to stop).

(iii) The car stops exactly at Q. Find the distance from P to Q.
It takes 4 seconds to go from P to Q.

$$s = 12t - \frac{3}{2}t^2 \quad \text{(distance in terms of time } t)$$

$$s = 12(4) - \frac{3}{2}(4)^2 \quad \text{(put in } t = 4)$$

$$s = 48 - 24$$

$$s = 24$$

$\therefore$ The distance from P to Q is 24 m.

(iv) Acceleration of the car

$$\text{Speed} = \frac{ds}{dt} = 12 - 3t$$

$$\text{Acceleration} = \frac{d^2s}{dt^2} = -3$$

$\therefore$ The acceleration of the car $= -3$ m/s^2.　　(minus means 'slowing down')

key point

When speed is in metres per second (ms^{-1}) and time is in seconds (s), the units of acceleration are metres per second per second written m/s^2 or m/s^{-2}.

exam Q

A marble is dropped from the top of a 15-storey building. The height of the marble above the ground, in metres, after t seconds is given by the formula:

$$h(t) = 44.1 - 4.9t^2$$

(i) Find the speed at which the marble hits the ground.

　　Give your answer:　　**(a)** in metres per second

　　　　　　　　　　　　(b) in kilometres per hour.

(ii) Using calculus or otherwise, write down the acceleration of the marble.

Solution

(i)　**(a)** When the marble hits the ground the height is zero

$$\therefore \quad h(t) = 44.1 - 4.9t^2$$

$$\Rightarrow \quad 0 = 44.1 - 4.9t^2$$

$$4.9t^2 = 44.1$$

$$t^2 = 9$$

$$t = 3 \text{ secs to hit the ground}$$

$$\text{Speed} = h'(t) = -2(4.9)t' = -9.8t$$

when $t = 3$, then $h'(3) = -9.8(3) = -29.4$ ms^{-1}

exam focus

Here, the 15-storey building is not relevant to the solution. Exam questions may include irrelevant information.

Hence, we say the speed of the marble when it hits the ground is 29.4 m/sec. (The minus sign indicates the marble is travelling down. This is not required for the speed.)

(b) $29 \cdot 4\,\text{ms}^{-1} = \dfrac{29 \cdot 4 \times 60 \times 60}{1,000}\,\text{km/h}^{-1}$

$= 105 \cdot 84\,\text{km/h}^{-1}$

(ii) Since $h'(t) = -9 \cdot 8t$ then acceleration $= h''(t)$

$= -9 \cdot 8\,\text{m/s}^{-2}$

key point

1,000 m = 1 km

60 × 60 secs = 1 hour

exam Q

The height, s, in metres after t seconds of a hailstone in a storm cloud is modelled by

$$s = 2473 - 45t + 27t^2 - 3t^3$$

Find:

(i) Its speed after t seconds
(ii) Its acceleration after t seconds
(iii) Its acceleration when the speed is zero

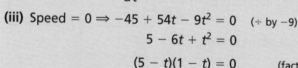

Time in seconds

Solution

(i) $s = 2473 - 45t + 27t^2 - 3t^3$

$\text{Speed} = \dfrac{ds}{dt} = -45 + 54t - 9t^2$

(ii) $\text{Acceleration} = \dfrac{d^2 s}{dt^2} = 54 - 18t$

(iii) Speed $= 0 \Rightarrow -45 + 54t - 9t^2 = 0$ ($\div$ by -9)

$5 - 6t + t^2 = 0$

$(5 - t)(1 - t) = 0$ (factorising)

$\therefore\ 5 - t = 0 \ \boxed{\text{or}}\ 1 - t = 0$

$5 = t \quad \boxed{\text{or}} \quad 1 = t$

$\text{Acceleration} = \dfrac{d^2 s}{dt^2} = 54 - 18t$

Put $t = 5$ into	Put $t = 1$ into
$\text{Acceleration} = \dfrac{d^2 s}{dt^2} = 54 - 18(5)$	$\text{Acceleration} = \dfrac{d^2 s}{dt^2} = 54 - 18(1)$
$= 54 - 90$	$= 54 - 18$
$= -36\,\text{ms}^{-2}$	$= +36\,\text{ms}^{-2}$
minus sign $\Rightarrow$ slowing down	plus sign $\Rightarrow$ speeding up

Rates of change in other situations

In addition to questions on displacement, velocity and acceleration, differential calculus can be used to solve other practical problems. We next consider various other practical problems where differential calculus may be used.

No matter what type of practical question we are asked, they will all have one key thing in common:

They ask for the rate at which some quantity changes.

In each case, this **rate is a derivative** that has to be calculated from the rate at which some other quantity is known to change.

i.e. find $\dfrac{dy}{dx}$, $h'(t)$, $\dfrac{dv}{dt}$ and get busy substituting the given values.

Example

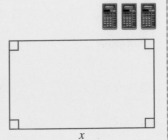

A rectangle has a perimeter of 84 cm. If one side has length x cm:

(i) Find the length of the other side in terms of x

(ii) Hence, find an expression for the area of the rectangle in terms of x

(iii) Find the maximum possible area of the rectangle as x varies

Solution

(i)

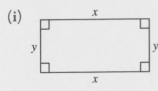

Let y = the length of the other side

$$\text{Perimeter} = x + y + x + y$$
$$84 = 2x + 2y$$
$$42 = x + y$$
$$42 - x = y$$

Now the length of the other side is $(42 - x)$.

(ii) A = area = (length)(breadth) = $(x)(42 - x) = 42x - x^2$

(iii) $A = 42x - x^2$

$$\frac{dA}{dx} = 42 - 2x$$

$$\frac{dA}{dx} = 0 \text{ for maximum}$$

By comparision $42 - 2x = 0$

$$42 = 2x$$

$$21 = x$$

$$\frac{d^2A}{dt^2} = -2 \text{ indicates there is a maximum value of } A \text{ at } x = 21.$$

When $x = 21 \Rightarrow A = 42(21) - (21)^2 \ A = 882 - 441 = 441\text{cm}^2$ maximum possible area.

$21 \times 21 = 441\text{cm}^2 \Rightarrow$ the rectangle with a maximum area is a square.

A farmer is growing winter wheat. The amount of wheat she will get per hectare depends on, among other things, the amount of nitrogen fertiliser that she uses. For her particular farm, the amount of wheat depends on the nitrogen in the following way:

$Y = 7{,}000 + 32N - 0{\cdot}1N^2,$

where Y is the amount of wheat produced, in kg per hectare, and N is the amount of nitrogen added in kg per hectare.

  (i) How much wheat will she get per hectare if she uses 100 kg of nitrogen per hectare?

 (ii) Find the amount of nitrogen that she must use in order to maximise the amount of wheat produced.

(iii) What is the maximum possible amount of wheat produced per hectare?

(iv) The farmer's total costs for producing the wheat are €1,300 per hectare. She can sell the wheat for €160 per tonne. She can also get €75 per hectare for the leftover straw. If she achieves the maximum amount of wheat, what is her profit per hectare?

Solution

(i) Substitute $N = 100$ into $Y = 7{,}000 + 32N - 0{\cdot}1N^2$
$$Y = 7{,}000 + 32(100) - 0{\cdot}1(100)^2$$
$$Y = 7{,}000 + 3{,}200 - 1{,}000$$
$$Y = 9{,}200 \text{ kg h}^{-1}$$

(ii) $Y = 7{,}000 + 32N - 0{\cdot}1N^2$

$\dfrac{dY}{dN} = 32 - 0{\cdot}2N$

$\dfrac{dY}{dN} = 0$ for a maximum

By comparison $32 - 0{\cdot}2N = 0$
$$320 - 2N = 0$$
$$320 = 2N$$
$$160 = N$$

$\therefore$ To achieve a maximum yield, apply 160 kg/h^{-1}.

$\dfrac{dY}{dN} = 32 - 0{\cdot}2N \Rightarrow \dfrac{d^2Y}{dN^2} = -0{\cdot}2,$

which indicates a maximum. This was not required in this question because of the word 'find'. However, if the question asked to 'show', then $\dfrac{d^2Y}{dN^2}$ would probably be required for full marks.

(iii) Maximum yield occurs when $N = 160$ kg h^{-1} is applied.

Hence, we put $N = 160$ into $Y = 7{,}000 + 32N - 0{\cdot}1N^2$

$$Y = 7{,}000 + 32(160) - 0{\cdot}1(160)^2$$
$$Y = 7{,}000 + 5{,}120 - 2{,}560 = 9{,}560 \text{ kg}$$

(iv)

Income	Expenses
From wheat per hectare	€1,300 per hectare
$= 160 \times 9{\cdot}560$ tonnes	
$= €1{,}529{\cdot}60$	

key point

1,000 kg = 1 tonne

From straw per hectare $= €75$

Profit $=$ income $-$ expenditure
$$= €1{,}529{\cdot}60 + €75 - €1{,}300 = €304{\cdot}60 \text{ per hectare}$$

exam Q

Investments can increase or decrease in value. The value of a particular investment of €100 was found to fit the following model:

$$V = 100 + 45t - 1{\cdot}5t^2$$

where V is the value of the investment in euro and t is the time in months after the investment was made.

(i) Find the rate at which the value of the investment was changing after six months.

Solution

key point

$V = 100 + 45t - 1{\cdot}5t^2$

$\dfrac{dV}{dt} = 45 - 3t$

'Rate' $\Rightarrow$ Find $\dfrac{dV}{dt}$.

Now put $t = 6$ to get $\left.\dfrac{dV}{dt}\right|_{t=6}$

$= 45 - 3(6)$
$= 45 - 18$
$= €27 \text{ per month}$

exam focus

This part (i) was awarded 5 marks.

(ii) State whether the value of the investment was increasing or decreasing after 18 months. Justify your answer.

Solution

$$\frac{dV}{dt} = 45 - 3t \text{ then,}$$

evaluate $\frac{dV}{dt}\Big|_{t=18}$

$$= 45 - 3(18)$$
$$= 45 - 54$$
$$= -€9 \text{ per month}$$

A negative value indicates decreasing. The above work is my justification.

This part (ii) was awarded 5 marks.

(iii) The investment was cashed in at the end of 24 months. How much was it worth at that time?

Solution

Put $t = 24$ into $V = 100 + 45t - 1·5t^2$

$$V = 100 + 45(24) - 1·5(24)^2$$
$$V = 100 + 1,080 - 864$$
$$V = €316$$

This part (iii) was awarded 25 marks! You can see from this instance how vital it is to attempt every question.

(iv) How much was the investment worth when it had its maximum value?

Solution

$$V = 100 + 45t - 1·5t^2$$

$$\frac{dV}{dt} = 45 - 3t = 0 \text{ for a maximum value}$$

$$45 = 3t$$
$$15 = t$$

We state that at $t = 15$ months, the investment is at the maximum.

Put $t = 15$ into $V = 100 + 45t - 1·5t^2$

$$\Rightarrow V = 100 + 45(15) - 1·5(15)^2$$
$$\Rightarrow V = 100 + 675 - 337·5 = €473·50$$

This part (iv) was awarded 5 marks.

The total revenue, R, obtained in (€000) from selling x hundred items on a particular day is given by the function

$$R = 20x - 2x^2.$$

(i) Find the total number of items sold in one day that will maximise the total revenue.

(ii) Hence, evaluate this total revenue.

Solution

(i) $R = 20x - 2x^2 \Rightarrow \dfrac{dR}{dx} = 20 - 4x$

For a maximum $\dfrac{dR}{dx} = 0$

By comparison $0 = 20 - 4x$

$4x = 20$

$x = 5$ (hundred, from the question)

key point

The word 'maximum' in the question

$\Rightarrow$ Find $\dfrac{dR}{dx}$ and then solve $\dfrac{dR}{dx} = 0$.

Answer: 500 items sold in a day.

(ii) The value of this total revenue is found by substituting $x = 5$ into R.

$\Rightarrow R = 20x - 2x^2$ becomes $R = 20(5) - 2(5)^2$

$R = 100 - 50$

$R = 50$ (€000, from the question)

Answer: The maximum revenue (obtained by selling 500 items) is €50,000.

Garden paving slabs measure 40 cm by 20 cm. The slabs are to be arranged to form a rectangular paved area. There are x slabs along one side and y slabs along an adjacent side, as shown.

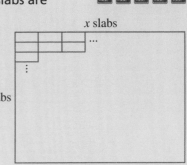

(i) Write the length of the perimeter, in centimetres, in terms of x and y.

(ii) The material being used for edging means that the perimeter is to be 64 metres. Find y in terms of x.

(iii) Find the value of x for which the paved area is as large as possible.

(iv) Find the number of slabs needed to pave this maximum area.

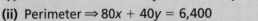

Solution

(i) Perimeter $= 40x + 20y + 40x + 20y = 80x + 40y$

(ii) Perimeter $\Rightarrow 80x + 40y = 6,400$

$$2x + y = 160 \quad \text{(divide by 40)}$$
$$y = 160 - 2x$$

> **key point**
>
> 64 m $= 64 \times 100 = 6,400$ cm

(iii) Area $= A = (40x)(20y) = 800xy = 800x(160 - 2x)$

$$A = 128,000x - 1,600x^2$$

$$\frac{dA}{dx} = 128,000 - 3,200x$$

$$\frac{dA}{dx} = 0 \quad \text{for a maximum}$$

> **key point**
>
> As large as possible means maximum $\Rightarrow$ we must solve $\dfrac{dA}{dx} = 0$ where A area.

By comparison $0 = 128,000 - 3,200x$

$$3,200x = 128,000 \quad \text{(divide by 3,200)}$$
$$x = 40$$

(iv) If $x = 40$ slabs then $y = 160 - 2x$

$$\Rightarrow y = 160 - 2(40) = 160 - 80 = 80 \text{ slabs}$$

Hence, the maximum number of slabs $= 40 \times 80 = 3,200$ slabs.

exam focus

This question was very poorly answered by candidates. All four parts were worth a total of 10 marks with 6 marks awarded for any one correct part. In the exam, keep going, attempt each part, do not become disheartened and you will do well.